The Biology of the Striped Skunk

The Biology of the Striped Skunk

B. J. Verts

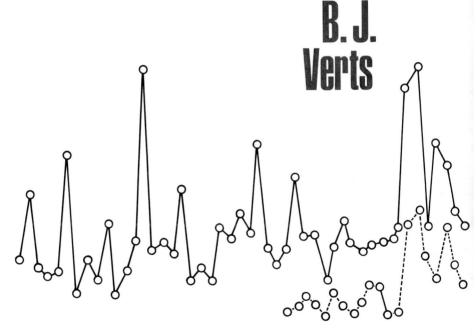

University of Illinois Press
Urbana · Chicago · London, 1967

PREFACE

The increase in numbers of cases of rabies involving wildlife species, reported by public health agencies in the United States during the early 1950's, was cause for concern among wildlife researchers and epidemiologists. Basic to this concern was the lack of adequate knowledge of the epizootiology of the disease among wildlife species.

Dr. Thomas G. Scott, then Head of the Section of Wildlife Research, Illinois Natural History Survey, developed an interest in rabies while working on the ecology of the red fox in Iowa. When Dr. Carl O. Mohr joined the staff of the Section of Wildlife Research as leader of the Mammal Branch, after several years' service with the U.S. Public Health Service, he was encouraged by Dr. Scott's keen interest in wildlife rabies to prepare a project proposal for research on several facets of the epizootiology of rabies in wildlife species in Illinois. This proposal was favorably considered by the U.S. Public Health Service and was funded by that agency. The project, a cooperative program administered jointly by the Section of Wildlife Research, Illinois Natural History Survey, and the College of Veterinary Medicine, University of Illinois, was initially guided by Dr. Mohr and Dr. Paul D. Beamer as co-principal investigators.

I was associated with the project as Research Associate and Field Mammalogist and was assigned to conduct the field studies. Field headquarters for the project were established in the northwestern part of the state on the campus of Shimer College, Mt. Carroll, Illinois. Choice of this geographic location was based on the long history of rabies in skunks in neighboring Iowa and Wisconsin.

The original objective of the research was to determine the prevalence and degree of interspecific transmission of rabies among various species of carnivorous and insectivorous mammals in northwestern Illinois. The objective was modified on June 1, 1959, when it had become evident that a clear-cut picture of the epizootiology of rabies could not be obtained by randomly sampling populations of the most common wild carnivores in the area, for up to that date rabies was not identified in tissues of specimens of any species of mammal caught. Because the reported incidence of rabies among striped skunks in the Midwest exceeded by several times the incidence among all other species of wild mammals combined, emphasis of the research was then directed toward evaluating the role of the striped skunk in the epizootiology of the disease. Almost at once it became apparent that basic knowledge concerning the life history and ecology of the striped skunk was insufficient for interpreting the results of the investigation. The primary objective, then, between June, 1959, and the termination of field work on August 31, 1962, was to study the life history of the striped skunk and to relate the knowledge obtained to the prevalence of rabies among populations of striped skunks in northwestern Illinois.

Dr. C. O. Mohr, recently retired from the Department of Entomology and Parasitology, University of California (Berkeley), Dr. T. G. Scott, present Head of the Department of Fisheries and Wildlife, Oregon State University, and Dr. G. C. Sanderson, Head, Section of Wildlife Research, Illinois Natural History Survey, served successively as principal investigator of the research project, representing the Illinois Natural History Survey. Their advice, guidance, and constructive criticisms were invaluable.

My co-workers at the Illinois Natural History Survey, especially Dr. R. D. Lord, Jr., Dr. R. R. Graber, Mr. W. W. Cochran, and Mr. G. L. Storm; my field assistants, particularly Mr. K. P. Dauphin; and many members of the faculty and staff of the College of Veterinary Medicine, University of Illinois, made valuable suggestions and cooperated in other ways. Dr. G. C. Sanderson and Helen C. Schultz, Illinois Natural History Survey, gave editorial assistance, and Marthanne Norgren, Department of Fisheries and Wildlife, Oregon State University, helped prepare the index.

The cooperation of President F. J. Mullin and of the faculty and staff of Shimer College is gratefully acknowledged.

The Illinois Department of Conservation, Illinois State Police, Illinois Rural Letter Carriers Association, Illinois Department of Agriculture, Illinois Department of Public Health, Iowa Conservation Commission, Iowa Department of Health, and Iowa Highway Patrol assisted in various capacities on different occasions during the study.

This research was supported by Public Health Service grants No. CC 00047 from the Communicable Disease Center and Nos. Al 01349 and E-1349 from the National Institute of Allergy and Infectious Diseases.

This work was submitted to the Graduate School, Southern Illinois University, as partial fulfillment of the requirements of the Doctor of Philosophy degree in the Department of Zoology. Dr. W. D. Klimstra, Professor of Zoology and Director of the Cooperative Wildlife Research Laboratory, served as major advisor of my graduate work.

B. J. VERTS
Oregon State University

CONTENTS

Chapter XII RABIES 144

Chapter I

THE STRIPED SKUNK

The striped skunk, *Mephitis mephitis* (Schreber), is a North American member of the Family Mustelidae occurring throughout southern Canada, United States (except for portions of the arid southwest), and extreme northern Mexico (Hall and Kelson 1959:935, Map 473). The species has been recorded at elevations from sea level to 13,800 feet (Nelson 1930:81), but Grinnell *et al.* (1937:322) reported that it is rare above 6,000 feet.

Two of the 13 subspecies of striped skunks currently recognized are reported to occur in Illinois (Hall and Kelson 1959:934-937, Miller and Kellogg 1955:754-758). *M. m. avia* Bangs is reported to occur in the western two-thirds of the state except in the southern tip, and *M. m. nigra* (Peale and Palisot de Beauvois) is reported to occur in the eastern one-third and in the southern tip of the state. Cory (1912:336) reported that the range of *M. hudsonica* (Richardson) (= *M. m. hudsonica* Richardson) extended northward from the northern edge of Illinois throughout Wisconsin. Jackson (1961:376) reported that all specimens from Wisconsin which he examined were referable to *M. m. hudsonica* but that about 10 percent of the specimens from southeastern Wisconsin exhibited some characteristics of *M. m. avia*. Miller and Kellogg (1955:756) stated that the boundaries of the range of *M. m. avia* were imperfectly known. According to the descriptions provided by Bangs (1896:140), Cory (1912:336-337), and Hamilton (1943: 162), specimens collected in northwestern Illinois during this study were not readily assignable to either *M. m. avia* or *M. m. hudsonica*. I suspect that comparison of specimens taken in northwestern Illinois with those from other parts of the state and from Wisconsin and Iowa would reveal that striped skunks in northwestern Illinois were intergrades between *M. m. avia* and *M. m. hudsonica,* with possibly some traces of *M. m. nigra.* Therefore, I have taken the conservative position of not assigning subspecific designation to striped skunks in northwestern Illinois.

DESCRIPTION OF THE SPECIES *MEPHITIS MEPHITIS* (SCHREBER)

Appearance

The striped skunk is about the size of the domestic cat, with a triangular-shaped head tapering to a rounded, nearly ball-shaped, nose pad. Its ears are small and rounded, and its small, beady black eyes are without readily discernible pupils. There are no nictitating membranes, a unique feature among carnivores (Smythe 1961:96). The legs are short, somewhat longer in the rear than in front, and the feet are plantigrade. The five digits on the front feet are equipped with long curved claws; the five toes on the rear feet have shorter and straighter claws. The skunk's tail is long and bushy. Striped skunks are equipped with a pair of scent glands, one on each side of the anus; strong encapsulating muscles are capable of propelling musk, produced and stored in the glands, for several feet through papillae protrusible through the anal opening.

The head and body of the striped skunk are glossy black, except for a narrow white stripe extending from the base of the nose pad to the forehead, and a rounded white patch on the pate extending as a single white bar to the shoulders, where it splits into two bars of variable length. There may be some white hairs in the tail; occasionally there is a small white patch on the chest.

In dorsal view, the short, heavy skull of the striped skunk is shaped much like a triangle and a trapezoid attached base to base. The zygomata are widest posteriorly and taper anteriorly. The mastoid regions are not inflated, but the mastoidal processes project laterally as prominent spines. In lateral view, the skull is convex superiorly with an inflated frontal region and a truncate rostrum; saggital and lamboidal crests are prominent on skulls of older animals. The auditory bullae are only slightly inflated. Infraorbital foramina are small and sometimes divided by thin septa. The palate is short, with a square posterior border about even with the posterior ends of the toothrows; a spine, double spines, a notch, or both double spines and notch may be present on the posterior edge of the palate. The mandible is squarish, with an obvious notch posteriorly. The teeth are relatively heavy, and the upper rear molars are somewhat dumbbell shaped. The tooth formula is

$$I \frac{3\text{-}3}{3\text{-}3}, \quad C \frac{1\text{-}1}{1\text{-}1}, \quad P \frac{3\text{-}3}{3\text{-}3}, \quad M \frac{1\text{-}1}{2\text{-}2} = 34.$$

Female striped skunks are reported to usually have six pairs of mammae (Cahalane 1947:213, Burt 1946:149, Leopold 1959:453), although Seton (1909:975, Fig. 228) depicted a female with 11 mammae, and Burt (1946:270, Appendix, Table IV) gave the range in number of mammae as 10 to 14. In April, 1962, it was noted that a captive female skunk had 13 mammae (Fig. 1), and that her only female offspring had 15 mammae (7 + 8). After that date, a record was kept of the number and arrangement of the mammae of all wild female striped skunks caught: In 12 of 23 (52.1 percent) the number of mammae observed was other than the "normal" six pairs; five had 11 (5 + 6), one had 12 (5 + 7), four had 13 (6 + 7), one had 14 (7 + 7), and one had 15 (7 + 8). Apparently, the number and arrangement of mammae in the striped skunk can be more variable than reported previously.

Striped skunks are probably best known by the characteristic odor of their musk. The musk is a yellowish, oily, phosphorescent substance sometimes containing creamy yellow "curds." This malodorous compound (chemically, butylmercaptan) can be detected by humans at a dilution of 5.8×10^{-9} mg per cc of air (Aldrich 1896:338). Its odor has been detected 20 miles from the nearest land (Cory 1912:343). Taken internally, butylmercaptan acts as a depressant of the central nervous system and, in large amounts, is reported to produce unconsciousness (Jackson 1961:378). Musk causes an intense burning sensation when brought into contact with the eyes but, contrary to popular beliefs, causes no permanent deleterious effects.

Etymology

The scientific name of the striped skunk, *Mephitis*, is derived from the Latin word *mephit*, meaning "bad odor" (Jaeger 1955:153).

The origin of the word "skunk" is reported to be an adaptation of the Abenaki Indian (Algonquin linguistic family) word "segankw or segongw," but variant forms of these names occur in many other Indian dialects (Philological Society 1933:158). The word "striped" refers to the color markings on the bodies of typical representatives of the species.

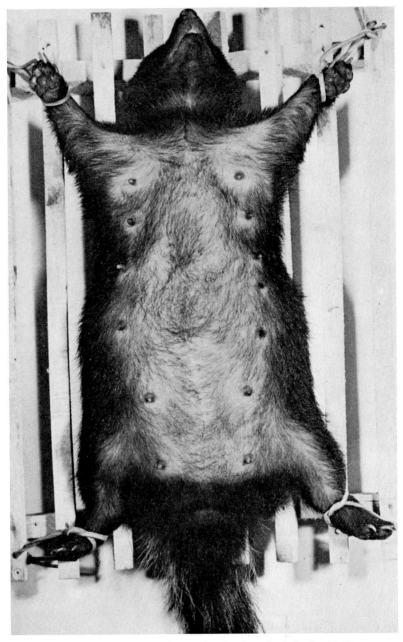

Fig. 1. Photograph of the venter of a captive female striped skunk with 13 mammae. The only female offspring of this female had 15 mammae.

History

The reference by Gabriel Sagard (1636:748) to "enfans du diable" (*sic*) is frequently cited as the first reference to the striped skunk in North America (Coues 1877:220, Cory 1912:335, Seton 1926:312-313). Although Fray Bernardino de Sahagun, a Franciscan friar who went to Mexico in 1529, mentioned that the Indians had several superstitions concerning skunks (Nuttall 1895:120), his reference could have been to skunks other than *Mephitis mephitis*, while that of Sagard could have referred to no other species.

Long before the arrival of white men in North America, striped skunks were used by the Indians for food and medicine (Coues 1877:212, Mooney 1900:255-256), as accessories in religious ceremonies (Henderson and Harrington 1914:24), and as the subject of art (Wyman 1952:2-3) and songs (Densmore 1923:93-94). Striped skunks were also the subject of many Indian superstitions and myths (Kroeber 1900:161-190, Bourke 1894:139, Jones 1911:233, Nuttall 1895:120), parts of which have been incorporated into the culture of modern America. For example, the name of one of our largest cities, Chicago, was adapted from the Fox Indian word meaning "the Place-of-the-Skunk," from a myth about a huge skunk killed on the southwestern shore of Lake Michigan (Jones 1911:233).

Pioneers in America apparently did not often use the flesh of striped skunks for food, but the scent and an oil rendered from the fat were used frequently for treatment of various diseases (Hyatt 1935:210, 236, 242, 264, 271; Coues 1877:213, Cahalane 1947:215). Because of a lack of understanding of the skunk, particularly of its ability to scent, many superstitions and misconceptions about the species arose (Coues 1877:211). Some of these misconceptions persist in modern America. (I have talked with several people who believe that the urine of the skunk is its musk.)

About 40-50 years ago, when articles of clothing trimmed with fur were in vogue, fur pieces made from striped skunk pelts were sold as "black sable" (Laut 1921:134). About this time, "skunk farming" became a popular sideline for farmers (Jones 1914:105-109, Laut 1921:134, Ashbrook 1928:122) but was apparently never very profitable because of the high initial investment required (Jones 1914:106-108).

At the present time, there apparently is little demand for striped skunks for fur or food. However, as recently as 1962, recipes for preparing skunk flesh for food were published (somewhat in jest) in a southern Illinois newspaper (Lane 1962:6). Other than the value of striped skunks as predators of species detrimental to the interests of man, of the very few "deodorized" skunks sold for pets, and of their status as an interesting species of our native fauna, the greatest value of the species appears to be as the perennial subject of jokes and cartoons.

Knowledge of the biology of the striped skunk appears to be incongruous with its past or present importance as a furbearer, as a reservoir and vector of zoonoses, with its nearly continental distribution, its distinctive color and odor, and its popularity as a subject of folklore, jokes, and cartoons. Other than the studies of Seton (1926), Wight (1931), Hamilton (1936), Selko (1937, 1938), Allen (1939), Jones (1939), Allen and Shapton (1942), and Shadle (1956), none of which were comprehensive, literature pertaining to the striped skunk consists primarily of popular articles based on these studies, and brief notes concerning minor aspects of the ecology and behavior of the species. All regional works on mammals in the United States mention the striped skunk, but much of the life history of the species included in them appears to have been based on the studies mentioned previously.

METHODS OF STUDY

This investigation of the striped skunk was begun October 1, 1957, and was terminated May 30, 1965. Field work was begun December 1, 1957, and completed August 31, 1962.

Systematic trapping operations were conducted on an area of about 516 square miles in Carroll and Whiteside counties, Illinois, to determine the relative abundance of striped skunks in various habitat types, to obtain indices to skunk population levels, and to obtain specimens of skunks and other species for testing for the presence of rabies virus. Approximately 50 No. 1½ steel traps per township (36 square miles) were placed in culverts along secondary roads. Road culverts in which traps were set were chosen on the basis of distribution within each township; distribution of traps was as uniform as possible. Traps, baited with a mixture of sardines, vegetable oil, and fox lure (Verts 1961a:283), were allowed to remain in place for four consecutive nights. Traps were examined each morning, the trapped animals were removed, and the traps were reset and rebaited. These operations were conducted in August, September, and October, 1958, and repeated during March, April, and May of both 1959 and 1960. In April, May, and June, 1961, traps were set in road culverts in areas in which trapping success was highest during the previous three trapping periods. In April, May, and June, 1962, traps were set in road culverts throughout the area, but the systematic procedure was abandoned in favor of lines of traps which were more easily attended.

On the basis of the distribution of the capture sites of striped skunks during the 1958 and 1959 trapping periods, an area was chosen for further study of striped skunk populations. This study area, hereafter referred to as the Shannon Study Area, was located in an intensively cultivated portion of Carroll County, about 1½ miles north of Shannon, Illinois. Livetrapping operations were conducted on the Shannon Study Area during late spring, summer, and early autumn each year between 1959 and 1962. During 1959 and 1960, striped skunks caught in live traps were marked with No. 3 monel fingerling tags[1] before they were released. Because several skunks recaptured in 1959 and 1960 had lost one or both of the fingerling tags, aluminum ear tags[1] used for rabbits were used for marking skunks in 1961 and 1962; fewer of the aluminum tags were lost.

To procure specimens during winter, when weather conditions prevented the trapping procedures described above, steel traps were occasionally set in protected locations such as old buildings, piles of brush, lumber, or trash, and in protected gullies.

In the 5-year period between 1957 and 1962, 395 individual striped skunks were captured a total of 456 times. Data collected from these skunks constitute the basis for this report.

Special techniques used for determining particular types of specific information concerning events in the life history of the striped skunk are described in the sections dealing with the information obtained by their use.

Common and scientific names of vertebrate animals referred to in this study are listed in Table A, Appendix.

---

[1] Available from National Band and Tag Company, Newport, Kentucky.

Chapter II

EXTERNAL MORPHOLOGY

WEIGHTS AND MEASUREMENTS OF ADULTS

External Measurements

Means, standard errors of the means, and ranges of the measurements for total length, body length, tail, hind foot, and ear (from notch) of adult male and female striped skunks are shown in Table 1. Numbers of measurements are given for each category because measurements of mutilated parts were omitted. All measurements except body lengths were taken in the usual manner from freshly killed or anesthetized specimens; body lengths were obtained by subtracting tail lengths from total lengths.

All measurements except tail lengths averaged larger in males than in females. Mean total, body, and hind-foot lengths were significantly different between males and females ($P < 0.01$). Means of tail and of ear lengths were not significantly different between sexes.

Mean total, body, and hind-foot lengths of both male and female striped skunks caught in northwestern Illinois were significantly larger ($P < 0.01$) than comparable means listed by Allen (1939:215-216) for Michigan skunks. Mean tail lengths of both sexes were not significantly different from mean tail lengths of Michigan skunks. Allen (1939:212) identified striped skunks in his sample as *M. m. nigra*. Hamilton (1943:160-162) stated that *M. m. hudsonica* was the largest of the *Mephitis* group, while *M. m. nigra* was of moderate size, and *M. m. avia* was the smallest of the eastern striped skunks. Striped

Table 1. *External measurements, in millimeters, of adult striped skunks, northwestern Illinois, 1958–62.*

MEASUREMENT	MALES			FEMALES		
	No.	MEAN AND SE	RANGE	No.	MEAN AND SE	RANGE
Total Length	110	630.9±4.2	540–765	69	602.7±3.2	520–670
Body Length	110	407.1±3.1	320–478	71	377.9±3.2	302–450
Tail Length	108	222.9±2.1	175–305	68	224.9±3.2	173–307
Hind-Foot Length	111	75.2±0.4	66–85	71	70.9±0.4	59–78
Ear Length	110	29.8±0.1	25–35	71	29.2±0.2	25–33

skunks caught in northwestern Illinois appear to tend more toward *M. m. hudsonica* than toward *M. m. avia* in size.

Skull Measurements

Means, standard errors of the means, and ranges of eight measurements of skulls from 60 male and 53 female striped skunks collected in northwestern Illinois are shown in Table 2. Measurements were taken according to Hall (1955:293, Figs. 96 and 97). Dial calipers, calibrated to 0.1 mm, were used to obtain measurements; estimations of measurements to 0.01 mm were made.

All mean measurements of skulls were significantly greater ($P<0.01$) among males than among females, but overlap in ranges of skull measurements indicated that these measurements would not be highly useful criteria for separating sexes. Fifty-one (45.1 percent) of the 113

Table 2. *Eight measurements, in millimeters, of skulls of 60 male and 53 female adult striped skunks, northwestern Illinois, 1959–62.*

MEASUREMENT	MALES		FEMALES	
	MEAN AND SE	RANGE	MEAN AND SE	RANGE
Skull Length	79.23±0.38	72.00–87.97	73.45±0.27	69.50–77.17
Condylobasal Length	74.90±0.34	69.28–80.77	69.58±0.25	65.01–73.51
Zygomatic Breadth	48.98±0.27	45.33–54.48	44.83±0.20	42.10–47.24
Mastoidal Breadth	40.91±0.26	36.98–44.97	38.25±0.09	35.20–40.34
Postglenoid Length	26.79±0.17	23.85–30.04	24.89±0.11	23.15–27.91
Palatal Length	29.71±0.17	26.81–32.70	27.81±0.14	25.92–29.21
Length of Toothrows	29.26±0.13	27.00–32.16	27.81±0.12	25.93–29.46
Postorbital Constriction	19.47±0.17	16.89–22.80	18.73±0.14	16.55–21.24

skull lengths (the measurement with the greatest difference between means) fell within the range of overlap (Table 2).

Latimer (1937:379-391) measured skulls from 208 *M. m. avia* collected in Kansas. Four skull measurements (skull length, zygomatic breadth, mastoidal breadth, and postorbital constriction) of these specimens were made in the same manner as those of specimens collected in northwestern Illinois during this study. Among males, means of measurements of skull lengths and of mastoidal breadths were significantly greater ($P < 0.01$) among Illinois skunks than among those from Kansas. Means of measurements of zygomatic breadths and of postorbital constrictions were not significantly different between the two samples. Among females, means of measurements of skull lengths and of mastoidal breadths were significantly greater ($P < 0.01$) in the sample from Illinois, while the means of zygomatic breadths and of postorbital constrictions were significantly greater ($P < 0.01$) in the Kansas sample. These comparisons indicated that striped skunks from northwestern Illinois tended to have longer and narrower skulls than skunks from Kansas.

Body Weights

Mean monthly weights of 197 adult male and female striped skunks are presented in Table 3. The mean weight of males (6.2 ± 0.2 lb) was significantly greater than the average weight of females (4.4 ± 0.2 lb) ($P < 0.01$). Mean weights of both males and females were at a minimum in March and at a maximum in October; mean weights of both sexes between these months were significantly different ($P < 0.01$). Differences between means indicated that about 47.7 percent and 55.1 percent of autumn body weights were lost during the winter by males and females, respectively. Hamilton (1937:327) found that weight losses of skunks during winter in New York state were 13.8 percent for males and 38.0 percent for females. In Michigan, Allen (1939:217) found weight losses as great as 36.3 percent among marked males and 31.6 percent among marked females.

In a study of starvation among *Oryctolagus cuniculus* in Australia, Mykytowycz (1961:151) found weight losses among survivors averaged 19.3 and 23.5 percent of prestarvation weights for males and females, respectively. Hanson (1962:10-11) reported that weight losses among starved Canada geese were 43 to 46 percent of assumed initial body weights calculated from weights of geese shot by hunters. Jordan (1953:310-311) found that mallards succumbed after losing 45 to 60

Table 3. *Mean monthly weights, in pounds, of 115 male and 82 female adult striped skunks, northwestern Illinois, 1958–62.*

MONTH	MALES			FEMALES		
	NO.	MEAN	RANGE	NO.	MEAN	RANGE
January	0	–	–	2	3.9	3.0–4.8
February	8	5.8	4.4–7.9	3	4.1	3.3–5.0
March	12	4.6	3.0–6.8	6	3.1	2.6–3.9
April	26	5.5	3.8–7.5	19*	4.2	2.8–6.3
May	23	5.7	3.8–7.7	9*	4.4	3.2–6.2
June	7	5.1	4.6–6.3	12	3.9	2.6–5.7
July	3	6.8	6.4–7.4	7	3.5	2.8–4.5
August	5	6.3	4.9–7.3	8	4.8	3.6–6.2
September	7	8.3	5.6–11.0	2	5.0	3.5–6.5
October	14	8.7	5.6–11.7	9	6.9	5.0–8.6
November	6	7.7	6.0–9.9	5	5.8	4.7–7.5
December	4	6.7	5.5–8.0	0	–	–
Totals	115	6.2	3.0–11.7	82	4.4	2.6–8.6

* Includes pregnant females.

percent of their body weights and that individuals which had lost an average of 44 percent of their prestarvation weights recovered when fed. These comparisons suggest that weight losses among striped skunks during winter may have approached the critical maximum.

Female striped skunks gained weight in April and May, probably because of pregnancy, but they averaged only 0.4 pound heavier in July than in March. The failure of females to gain weight in June and July was probably caused by progressively increasing requirements (lactation and care) of the young. A substantial increase in the mean monthly weight of females began in August and continued through October; greatest gains were made during September and October.

Males apparently began to recover weight losses in April and continued to gain weight until October. Slight decreases in mean weights in June and August were probably due to chance variation within monthly samples. The greatest increases in mean weights of males occurred during August and September.

PELAGE

Striped skunks are probably best known by the unique odor of their musk and by the typical black and white pattern of their pelage. Color markings of few other mammals are as distinctive or as universally recognized in North America. Nevertheless, several characteristics of the pelage of striped skunks apparently have not been recorded.

Color and Morphology of Hairs

The pelage of striped skunks is composed of coarse, shiny guard hairs about 1.5 to 3 inches long which subtend an underfur of soft wavy hairs about 1 to 1.2 inches long. Hairs of the underfur within the black areas are black tipped, with dark-grayish bases; hairs forming the characteristic white stripes are uniformly white and are usually slightly longer than adjacent black hairs. The skin is grayish black beneath the black hairs and pinkish beneath the white hairs.

Guard hairs of both colors are multiple-fusiform and have fine imbricated scales (Austin 1922:25, Fig. 2B). The cortex of these hairs is

Fig. 2. Photomicrographs of hairs from a striped skunk. (A) Black dorsal guard hair (partly bleached). About 124 ×.

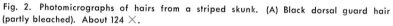

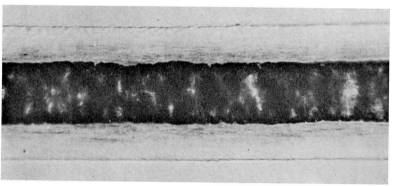

Fig. 2. (B) White dorsal guard hair. About 40 ×.

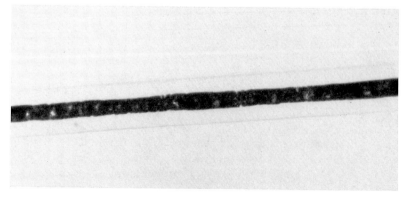

Fig. 2. (C) Black dorsal fur fiber (partly bleached). About 40 ✕.

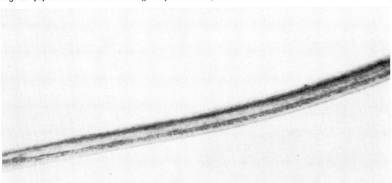

Fig. 2. (D) White dorsal fur fiber. About 50 ✕.

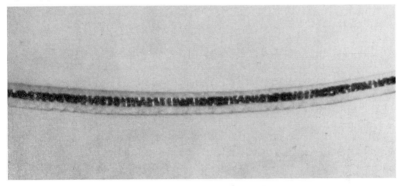

clear or only slightly pigmented; the medullae of guard hairs have single canals which appear to be incompletely divided by septa. Black guard hairs have deeply pigmented medullae; white guard hairs have small amounts of pigments in their medullae.

Fur fibers of the underfur of both colors are multiple-fusiform and have distinctly imbricated cuticular scales. The pigmentation of the cortex of these fibers is similar to the pigmentation of the guard hairs. Medullae of underfur fibers have single canals distinctly and completely divided by septa. Photomicrographs of guard hairs and fur fibers of both colors are shown in Figure 2.

Striped skunks of several colors other than black and white have been reported. Detlefsen and Holbrook (1921:248) reported striped skunks which were seal brown, white with black eyes, white with a small amount of pigment in the iris, and pure albino. They also recorded a yellow striped skunk but were unsure whether the pigment was natural or acquired.

Color Patterns

The amount and distribution of white in the pelage may vary considerably among individual striped skunks. The fur industry grades

Fig. 3. A classification of color patterns of striped skunks.

BLACK (STAR)

SHORT STRIPE

NARROW STRIPE

BROAD STRIPE

pelts of skunks according to the amounts of white that they contain; four grades are commonly used (Bachrach 1953:372). These are, in order of increasing amounts of white: black (star), short-striped, long-(narrow-)striped, and broad-striped (Fig. 3). Although this classification is somewhat arbitrary, color patterns of most striped skunks are readily assignable to one of the four grades.

Stains and Stuckey (1960:139) reported a striped skunk with brachial-antebrachial stripes. Diagrams of three pelts with aberrant color patterns, observed in northwestern Illinois, are shown in Figure 4.

Fig. 4. Atypical color patterns of three striped skunks caught in northwestern Illinois.

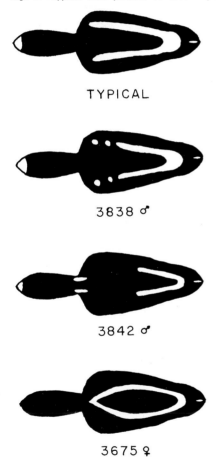

TYPICAL

3838 ♂

3842 ♂

3675 ♀

Bachrach (1953:378) stated that about 40 percent of skunk pelts from the central states were black and short-striped, about 35 percent narrow-striped, and about 25 percent broad-striped. Of 241 striped skunks caught in northwestern Illinois, the pelts of 202 (83.8 percent) were classified as narrow-striped. The percent of pelts assigned to each of the four color-pattern classes for each of the sexes is shown in Figure 5. No significant differences in markings of the sexes were noted. Jones (1950:29) examined 54 pelts of striped skunks taken in northeastern Kansas and recorded 2 black, 14 short-striped, 28 narrow-striped, and 10 broad-striped. This ratio was significantly different

Fig. 5. Percent frequency of each of the four color patterns observed among 130 male and 101 female striped skunks, northwestern Illinois, June, 1959–August, 1962. Hatched bars denote males.

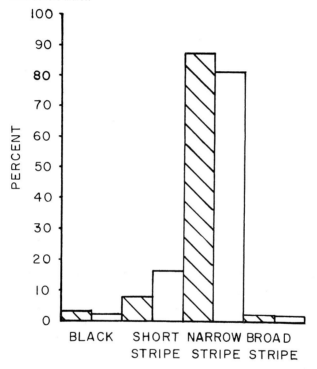

from the ratio found among striped skunks in northwestern Illinois ($P < 0.01$).

A tuft of white hairs (pencil) extending 1 to 3 inches beyond the black hairs of the tail was present on 55 (44.3 percent) of 124 striped skunks examined. Numbers of skunks with and without a pencil of white hairs are shown for each of the color-pattern classes in Table 4. There was no significant difference in the presence or absence of this character between sexes, but there were significant differences among

Table 4. *Numbers of striped skunks with and without a pencil of white hairs on the tail, in each of the four color-pattern classes.*

| | COLOR PATTERN | | | | |
CATEGORY	BLACK	SHORT-STRIPE	NARROW-STRIPE	BROAD-STRIPE	TOTALS
Female					
Pencil Present	2	5	19	2	28
Pencil Absent	0	1	31	1	33
Male					
Pencil Present	1	3	23	0	27
Pencil Absent	0	4	32	0	36
Both Sexes					
Pencil Present	3	8	42	2	55
Pencil Absent	0	5	63	1	69

color-pattern classes ($P < 0.02$) ; the pencil occurred most often among skunks with the least amounts of white in their fur.

Molts

Times and directions of molts were determined by coloring the white portions of adult captive striped skunks with picric acid and examining the skunks at irregular intervals for loss of the color. Molting began in April (males about 2 weeks later than females), when the underfur was shed. As the underfur was shed, it became entangled in unmolted guard hairs, and large wads of matted hair were formed. These wads of hair appeared first in the scapular region and later in the lumbar and pelvic regions. Similar wads of matted hair were observed on wild skunks at the same season. The appearance of the wads of matted hair and the loss of colored underfur progressed from anterior to posterior, indicating the direction of the molt. The underfur was not replaced at this time.

Molting of guard hairs began in July, at which time both underfur and guard hairs were replaced. The direction of the molt of guard hairs was also anterior to posterior. Replacement of both underfur and guard hairs was apparently completed by about the first of September.

Juvenile striped skunks apparently did not molt until they were approximately 11 to 12 months old.

Characteristics and Uses of Striped Skunk Fur

The usable portion of the average striped skunk pelt measures about 8 × 15 inches. After tanning and prior to use, the white portions of the pelt are removed (Bachrach 1953:371) or dyed the same color as the remainder of the pelt (Austin 1922:19). The pelt is "tipped" by dipping it into a weak blue dye to darken the leather and to improve the luster of the hair (Bachrach 1953:371). The resulting fur weighs about 2⅞ ounces per square foot and has a durability rating of 50, based on the rating of 100 for otter fur (Austin 1922:6).

Striped skunk fur is used for making coats and jackets and for trimming fur and cloth coats. The white stripes, when removed, are sewed together, dyed, and used for trimming various garments. Tails are used for manufacturing brushes, and the grease removed in processing skins is used in making soap (Bachrach 1953:378).

At the present time, long-haired furs are not particularly fashionable; consequently, there is little demand for striped skunk pelts.

Chapter III

GROWTH AND DEVELOPMENT

Three litters (18 individuals) of striped skunks born in captivity were examined when they were less than 24 hours old and at subsequent irregular intervals to determine the rate of growth and the sequence of development. Each individual in two litters (12 individuals) was weighed at 3-day intervals until the young were 60 days old. Daily observations were made to determine when certain events in development occurred, such as opening of the eyes and ears and the ability to expel musk.

PELAGE

Examination within 24 hours of birth revealed that the skin of the young skunks was pinkish in areas covered with white hairs and bluish black in areas covered with, or soon to be covered with, black hairs. Blood vessels, viscera, and cranial sutures were not visible through the skin.

Hairs on the dorsum were about 2-3 mm long at birth but only about 1 mm long and very sparse on the venter. The vibrissae were about 4 mm long and much stiffer than the body hairs. The pads of the feet, tip of the tail, ears, lips, and genital region were naked. No completely naked skunks were observed, as were reported by Seton (1926:353).

The hairs on the dorsum were 6-7 mm long when the young were 2 weeks old, 10-11 mm when 3 weeks old, 17-20 mm at 4 weeks of age, 27-32 mm at 5 weeks, and 30-36 mm when 6 weeks old. The venter was covered with hairs except at the midline and in the genital region when the young were 5 weeks old.

No postjuvenile molt was observed. The white hairs of a male 2 weeks old were colored with a permanent dye (Nyanzol A) and the tips of the hairs were still colored when the skunk was 5 months old.

EYES, EARS, AND CLAWS

The eyes of 12 striped skunks examined within 24 hours after birth were closed. The line of fusion of the lids was a visible furrow between two very slight ridges. In one litter, four of five young opened one or both eyes when 22 days old. In another litter, two of seven opened one or both eyes when 24 days old, but both eyes of all individuals in this litter were not open until the skunks were 35 days old. Seton (1926: 354) reported a litter whose members opened one or both eyes when 17 days old. Apparently, the eyes of striped skunks may open within a period of 2 weeks or more and thus are not a criterion of age.

When examined shortly after birth, ears of young skunks were closed by the tragi and by pinnae folded over the auditory canals. The pinnae unfolded and assumed the normal upright position within 5 or 6 days. The ears of four of the five young in one litter opened when the skunks were 24 days old, 2 days after the eyes opened. In the other litter, all seven had their ears open when 27 days old, 8 days before the last member of the litter opened its eyes.

At birth the claws were white, soft, and about 1.5 mm long. They darkened and hardened within 2-3 days.

DENTITION

Observations of the eruption of the teeth of skunks in one litter of five were made at 3-day intervals beginning 37 days after birth. No tooth eruptions were noted until the skunks were 40 days old, at which time all five young had teeth visible above the gum line. Because teeth in some individuals erupted at a slightly earlier age than corresponding teeth in other individuals, it was possible to determine the sequence of tooth eruptions (Table 5).

Direct examination, at 3-day intervals, of the teeth of captive striped skunks between 52 and 90 days old showed that the teeth which had begun to erupt when these skunks were 40 days old had not been replaced by others. The discovery of the skull of a skunk about 55 days old, with a tiny supernumerary tooth attached to the buccal side of

Table 5. The sequence of eruption of the dentition of five striped skunks born in captivity.

SEQUENCE	AGE IN DAYS	DENTAL FORMULAE			
1	40	I $\frac{2-2}{0-0}$,	C $\frac{0-0}{0-0}$,	P $\frac{0-0}{0-0}$,	M $\frac{0-0}{0-0}$
2	40	I $\frac{2-2}{2-2}$,	C $\frac{0-0}{0-0}$,	P $\frac{0-0}{0-0}$,	M $\frac{0-0}{0-0}$
3	40	I $\frac{3-3}{2-2}$,	C $\frac{0-0}{0-0}$,	P $\frac{0-0}{0-0}$,	M $\frac{0-0}{0-0}$
4	43	I $\frac{3-3}{3-3}$,	C $\frac{0-0}{0-0}$,	P $\frac{0-0}{0-0}$,	M $\frac{0-0}{0-0}$
5	43	I $\frac{3-3}{3-3}$,	C $\frac{0-0}{0-0}$,	P $\frac{2-2}{2-2}$,	M $\frac{0-0}{0-0}$
6	46	I $\frac{3-3}{3-3}$,	C $\frac{0-0}{1-1}$,	P $\frac{2-2}{2-2}$,	M $\frac{0-0}{0-0}$
7	46	I $\frac{3-3}{3-3}$,	C $\frac{1-1}{1-1}$,	P $\frac{2-2}{2-2}$,	M $\frac{0-0}{0-0}$
8	46	I $\frac{3-3}{3-3}$,	C $\frac{1-1}{1-1}$,	P $\frac{2-2}{3-3}$,	M $\frac{0-0}{0-0}$
9	49	I $\frac{3-3}{3-3}$,	C $\frac{1-1}{1-1}$,	P $\frac{3-3}{3-3}$,	M $\frac{1-1}{0-0}$
10	49	I $\frac{3-3}{3-3}$,	C $\frac{1-1}{1-1}$,	P $\frac{3-3}{3-3}$,	M $\frac{1-1}{1-1}$
11	52	I $\frac{3-3}{3-3}$,	C $\frac{1-1}{1-1}$,	P $\frac{3-3}{3-3}$,	M $\frac{1-1}{2-2}$

each upper canine (Fig. 6), led me to suspect that the teeth which began to erupt on the 40th day of life were not the deciduous dentition. Serial sections of the jaw of a striped skunk sacrificed on the day of birth revealed the presence of a tiny developing tooth, complete with enamel organ, distal to each of the larger incisors, canines, and premolars also undergoing development. These tiny teeth must either be shed or resorbed between the time of birth and the eruption of teeth beginning on the 40th day of life. Thus, although striped skunks are truly diphodont, only the "permanent" teeth become functional.

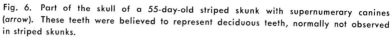

Fig. 6. Part of the skull of a 55-day-old striped skunk with supernumerary canines (arrow). These teeth were believed to represent deciduous teeth, normally not observed in striped skunks.

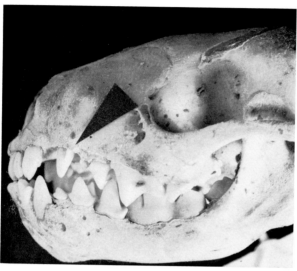

BEHAVIOR OF YOUNG SKUNKS

At birth, the young skunks were able to right themselves when placed on their backs. They made weak crawling movements but, because of poor coordination, were unable to propel themselves. The hind legs were usually held to the rear and were not used in crawling movements. The young did not cling to the teats of the female when she was forced to leave the nest box.

Young skunks frequently licked their lips and sometimes made clicking sounds with their tongues. The most commonly detected sounds were weak, mouselike squeaks and birdlike twitters. No evidence was noted that skunks were able to perceive light or sound at birth.

When 1 week old, young skunks were able to turn and roll easily, immediately righting themselves when placed on their backs. The sounds made when the adult female was absent were similar to those made earlier but were much louder and of longer duration.

Odor of musk was first detected when the young were 14 days old. (Scent glands had been removed from all adults in the captive colony.) A drop of yellow musk was noted at the anal opening of a male 17 days old. Whether musk was not expelled earlier because the papillae were closed or because muscular coordination was inadequate is not known; musk is present at birth.

Young skunks which had their ears open flinched when a ruler was gently slapped against a desk. At 3 weeks of age the young were able to move about with a swimming motion, with the hind legs still extended to the rear. At 25 days of age all five in one litter raised their tails in warning and ejected a drop or two of musk when the nest box

Fig. 7. Mean weights, at 3-day intervals, of 12 striped skunks born in captivity. Vertical lines indicate 95 percent confidence limits.

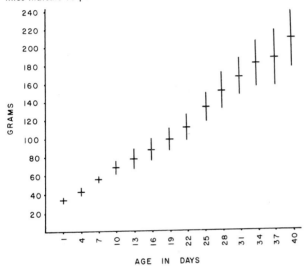

was opened. One of the five made a weak attempt to stamp its front feet — a typical warning signal of striped skunks. When 28 days old all five were able to support themselves shakily for a few moments and at 30 days of age two of the five were in the cage outside the nest box. The hind legs usually were extended to the rear between periods of standing.

At 38 days of age the five young skunks began to eat small bits of sardines; when 45 days old they ate sardines ravenously. The young were 50 days old when they first ate dry dog chow (food for the adult). When 60 days of age, the young were separated from their mother and each individual was placed in a separate cage. Food for the young was the same as for adults, dog chow and an occasional sardine.

Table 6. *Means and ranges of body measurements, in millimeters, taken at irregular intervals between birth and 43 days of age, of one litter of five striped skunks born in captivity.*

Age in Days	Total Length	Tail Length	Hind-Foot Length	Ear Length
1	131.4 (124–137)	37.2 (33–41)	16.6 (16–17)	4.0 (4)
13	157.0 (137–166)	44.6 (38–48)	20.0 (17–21)	7.6 (6–9)
22	188.0 (158–211)	54.8 (45–64)	24.2 (22–25)	11.2 (10–12)
28	266.0 (199–253)	71.0 (61–79)	29.0 (26–31)	14.6 (13–16)
36	251.0 (227–272)	82.0 (71–92)	35.0 (33–38)	19.0 (17–21)
43	273.8 (235–300)	91.0 (83–103)	38.4 (37–40)	21.0 (19–22)

GROWTH

Seton (1926:310), referring to striped skunks, stated: "At birth, they weigh about half an ounce; at 8 weeks 1½ lbs." The mean weight of 12 striped skunks weighed within 24 hours of birth was 33.4 (range 26.7–41.4) grams. Mean weights at 3-day intervals between birth and 40 days of age for these 12 skunks are shown in Figure 7. Sanderson (1961a:3) believed that weight gains of captive and of wild raccoons were similar before weaning. After 40 days of age, differences in intake of solid food by individual striped skunks caused wide variations in body weights among members of a single litter even though they continued to suckle their mother.

Means and ranges of body measurements of five young skunks, taken at irregular intervals between birth and 43 days of age, are presented in Table 6. The growth of one juvenile male is shown in a series of photographs taken at birth and at weekly intervals until the young skunk was 5 weeks old (Fig. 8).

Fig. 8. Photographs of a male striped skunk on the day of birth and at weekly intervals until 5 weeks old. (A) Day of birth.

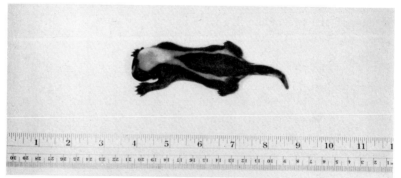

Fig. 8. (B) One week old.

Fig. 8. (C) Two weeks old.

Fig. 8. (D) Three weeks old.

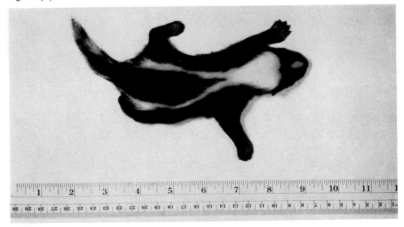

Fig. 8. (E) Four weeks old.

Fig. 8. (F) Five weeks old.

No wild skunk weighing less than 0.9 lb (407 grams) was captured in live traps. Most captive skunks attained this weight at about 52 to 55 days of age. From this fact, and from calculation of dates of parturition of pregnant females, it appears that skunks which weighed 1 pound were about 60 days old. Skunks of this weight were usually first captured during the first week of July each year. Growth of young wild

Fig. 9. Changes in weight of 22 wild juvenile striped skunks caught two or more times each, northwestern Illinois, 1959–62.

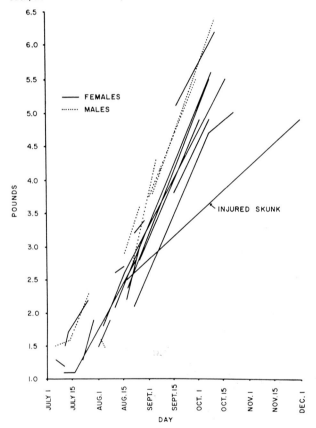

skunks weighed two or more times between the first week of July and November 30 was remarkably uniform (Fig. 9). One young female skunk which lost a hind leg failed to gain weight as rapidly as uninjured skunks.

Chapter IV

BEHAVIOR

Although many short notes have been published in which certain traits exhibited by striped skunks were considered, no comprehensive study of behavior of the species has been published. The present study was not intended to be comprehensive, but an attempt was made to verify and, when possible, to obtain quantitative data concerning some behavioral characteristics of striped skunks.

GENERAL DISPOSITION

In general, healthy striped skunks encountered during this study were unobtrusive; there were no indications that they were ever belligerent or pugnacious except toward their own kind during the breeding season. This characteristic docility of striped skunks may stem from their unique mechanism for defense.

It is often stated that striped skunks will "stand their ground" when approached by a man or a vehicle. Unless a skunk was caught in a trap or otherwise in a position where it appeared to be "cornered," I did not find this type of behavior to be the rule. At night, when caught in the beam of a spotlight or in the beams of headlights of a slow-moving vehicle, the first reaction of a skunk was to flee. If pursued, or if the vehicle was moving faster than about 20 miles per hour when the skunk was spotted, it would usually face the intruder and assume a defensive pose. Howell (1943:98-99) commented on the apparent confusion exhibited by skunks when caught in beams of automobile headlights and attributed the large number of road kills of skunks to this confusion. Of 11 striped skunks spotlighted at night from a vehicle moving at about 10 miles per hour, all attempted to flee; none attempted to "stand their ground" except when pursued, and none appeared to be particularly confused by the lights. At the present time, traffic on good highways moves at such speed that striped skunks probably attempt to flee oncoming vehicles, but, finding that they cannot escape, stand their ground and are struck.

In general, senses of sight, hearing, and smell of striped skunks appeared to be poor. Most skunks caught in live traps did not seem to be aware of approaching persons until they were within 5 or 6 feet of the traps. I have driven an automobile to within 3 feet of striped skunks busily engaged in attempting to escape from steel traps by digging, without eliciting responses. An adult male striped skunk once walked within a foot of me while I was standing motionless in an open field. On another occasion, I saw an adult female skunk nearly collide with a cock pheasant without appearing to notice the pheasant. I also observed two striped skunks, one an adult female, the other believed to be an adult female, meet and pass each other on the same path without indicating awareness of each other. Although these observations appear to represent examples of poor perception, it is difficult to distinguish some of them from examples of "single-mindedness."

WARNING BEHAVIOR AND DEFENSIVE POSES

When cornered or closely pursued, striped skunks usually faced the intruder, arched their backs, elevated their tails, erected the hairs of their tails, stamped the ground with their front feet, and shuffled backward. This behavior placed skunks in a favorable position for discharging their musk and warned intruders that musk would be discharged toward them unless they turned away.

Foot Stamping

Young skunks and pregnant or lactating adult females appeared particularly prone to stamp their front feet at the least disturbance. They arched their backs, standing with their rear feet relatively wide apart, and held the front feet close together while pounding them rapidly on the ground. The sound created by this action could often be heard several feet away when the skunks were on hard ground. Among young littermates this behavior was often directed toward one another, the only behavior observed which was interpreted as play.

Handstands

Standing and walking on the forefeet appears to be a characteristic warning pose of spotted skunks (Johnson 1921:87-89, Walker 1930: 227-229, Crabb 1948:230) but may occasionally be observed among striped skunks (Seton 1920:140). I observed young striped skunks, raised in captivity, frequently stand on their forefeet momentarily and occasionally take a step or two while in this position. Foot stamping and shuffling backward were commonly observed to occur prior to the attainment of handstands. When the forefeet were drawn backward, with the back arched in the foot-stamping posture, the center of balance of the animal was shifted anteriorly. Very little effort was then required to raise the rear legs from the ground. On many occasions I observed skunks in this position to shuffle backward and to rock back and forth on the front feet, the rear feet leaving the ground by no more than an inch. I did not observe handstands among older skunks or among wild skunks of any age.

Scenting

Probably more has been written, both factual and erroneous, concerning the ability of striped skunks to defend themselves by scenting (discharging musk) than about any other trait of the species. Dice (1921: 38) attempted to dispel the common misconception that skunks cannot scent while suspended by the tail. Allen and Neill (1955:6) stated that skunks can neither scent nor bite while suspended by the the tail, but 5 months later Phares (1956:22), in the same serial publication, stated that skunks can scent from this position. Apparently, there is some individual variation among striped skunks in the degree of provocation necessary to evoke the scenting response, or there is a lack of firsthand knowledge concerning the method of handling skunks. Two striped skunks which I attempted to handle by this method successfully and accurately scented while suspended by their tails.

Striped skunks apparently avoid fouling their fur with their musk and will usually not scent if their tails are held over their anal openings. A skunk will usually refrain from scenting if the anus is held against the ground tightly. Allen (1939:213-214) described a method of handling skunks without danger to the handler from biting or scenting. The skunks were grasped around the neck with one hand and by the base of the tail with the other. The animal was then turned on its back with the anal opening pointed away from the handler and downwind. I occasionally used this technique with young skunks successfully but did not attempt to use it with older skunks.

During 1960 and 1961, a record was kept of the frequency of scenting by striped skunks caught in traps and anesthetized with sodium pentobarbital administered with a syringe attached to a long pole (Verts 1960:335-336). Of 175 striped skunks handled by this method, 32 (18.3 percent) scented, but most did not expel more than a drop or two of musk. There were no significant differences in frequency of scenting among various sex and age groups, but those of us using the technique were agreed that adult males were somewhat more prone to scent than adult females or young of either sex. We may have biased these data by approaching larger skunks with greater caution.

Striped skunks can discharge musk in two forms: (1) an atomized spray in which the individual droplets are nearly invisible, and (2) a short stream which separates in flight into rain-sized drops, similar to the stream shot from a toy water gun. I once saw the atomized spray of musk when I shot a skunk which was in the shade but between the sun and me; the droplets drifted in the nearly motionless air like a puff of smoke. This form of discharge was uncommon; large drops were almost always observed when the odor of musk was detected. The streams of musk did not appear to be propelled directly toward an intruder but were discharged with a slight turning motion so that the drops of musk covered an arc of 30 to 45 degrees. By this means skunks greatly increased the probability of hitting intruders with their musk. I was once hit just below the waist by three drops of musk discharged by a skunk from a distance of about 10 feet; the drops were about 4 inches apart.

VOCALIZATION

Striped skunks are usually silent animals but can make a variety of sounds. Seton (1926:334) described sounds made by striped skunks as low churrings, growls, shrill screeches, birdlike twitters, and dovelike cooings. Laun (1962:432-433) described sounds made by captive skunks as short squeals, growls, and hissing noises. He also heard squeals similar to those made by domestic swine. Hall (1955:212) described sounds which he heard made by skunks as "something between a growl and a snarl."

In caring for a captive colony of striped skunks (5 to 18 animals) over a 3-year period, I heard sounds which could be described as churrings, growls, screeches, birdlike twitters, squeals, and hisses, but I did not hear any sounds quite so loud as those produced by swine. Young skunks were much more vociferous than adults. Pregnant or lactating females made hissing noises whenever they were disturbed, and usually uttered loud and persistent screeches when adult males were placed in cages with them. A few wild skunks were heard to make hissing noises when the traps in which they were caught were approached, but no other sounds were heard.

SWIMMING

Striped skunks usually avoid water but can swim when need arises. Cole (1921:6) reported that bathers in the Wisconsin River saw an adult and four young skunks swimming toward them from an island but that all five skunks returned to the island when they saw the bathers. Wilber and Widenbacher (1961:429) reported that skunks were able to swim for more than 7.5 hours in water at 22° C.

On July 27, 1959, a young skunk, when released from a live trap, traveled rapidly to a small stream about 200 yards away, drank, eased itself into the water, and swam downstream for approximately 50 yards. On two other occasions striped skunks were observed to swim across small streams. The swimming technique used by striped skunks was similar to that used by domestic dogs; only the head, above the level of the mouth, and the tail were visible above the surface of the water.

WALKING AND RUNNING

Striped skunks were observed to have three gaits: a gallop, a canter, and a pace. In the gallop, the two forelimbs and the two hindlimbs moved in unison; the hind feet struck the ground nearly parallel in front of the tracks made by the front feet (Murie 1954:78, Fig. 37f). This gait was used only when great speed was necessary. The canter, normally used when traveling to and from the feeding area, and occasionally while feeding, was characterized by easy bounds. The hind feet struck the ground alternately between tracks made by the front feet, creating a series of four tracks oblique to the direction of travel (Murie 1954:78, Fig. 37d). The pace, the slowest gait, was used primarily while feeding. In this gait the limbs moved in lateral pairs so that the animal was supported by the right and left legs alternately, accounting for the waddling gait commonly observed.

MacLulich (1936:92) timed running speeds of two skunks with an automobile speedometer and found that one ran about 6 miles per hour for 150 yards and the other at between 8 and 9 miles per hour for 100 yards. I was able to overtake and capture with a net several striped skunks when they were in low vegetation on solid ground, but I was unable to catch skunks when they were on freshly plowed ground or when I was encumbered by heavy clothes and boots. Estimates of the speed of skunks based on my running speed indicated that striped skunks could run short distances at about 10 miles per hour, a speed not appreciably greater than the estimates of MacLulich.

CLIMBING

Seton (1926:318) stated that striped skunks can climb no objects except woven-wire fences. I found no evidence that skunks could climb other objects. In captivity, only juveniles were observed to climb on the woven-wire sides of their cages.

PACING

Only one captive skunk, an adult male, was observed to pace back and forth along one side of his cage, as is frequently observed among captives of other species. This skunk performed an unusual ritual in which the widely spaced rear feet were held stationary on the floor of the cage and the front feet were alternately crossed over each other while the forward part of the body was swung back and forth. One spot in the cage was apparently preferred for performing this ritual; the wire at this spot in the cage was always bright from wear.

SHAKING

On September 12, 1961, a juvenile male striped skunk to which a radio transmitter had been attached was released during a rain. Before the skunk was lost from view, he was observed to stop and shake the water from his fur several times. These movements caused such distinctive changes in the signal pattern of the radio that subsequently it was possible to determine when shaking occurred by listening to the radio signal. Shaking occurred frequently on rainy nights or when the vegetation was covered with dew. On the night of October 12-13, 1961, during a heavy rainstorm, a female skunk shook herself at 3- to 5-minute intervals.

FEEDING

Several unusual and interesting feeding habits of striped skunks have been reported. Storer and Vansell (1935:118) reported that skunks scratched on the front of beehives to induce bees to leave their hives. The bees were then caught and eaten. Chapman (1946:397) observed skunks returning to their own droppings to capture beetles feeding thereon. King (1944:85) described an egg-opening technique of striped skunks whereby the egg was propelled by the front legs between the hind legs until it struck some hard object and was broken. Schmidt (1936:287) reported that skunks rolled caterpillars on the ground with their forepaws to remove the hairs before eating them and also rolled toads on the ground to remove the skin poison. Apparently, the more typical feeding behavior of striped skunks capturing beetles and grasshoppers has not been recorded.

During this investigation, two wild skunks were observed while they were feeding. An adult female to which a radio transmitter was attached was visually observed for about 10 minutes while she fed, beginning at 0352 hours on June 5, 1962, and from 0355 hours to 0402 hours on June 7, 1962. This skunk was feeding in a cornfield in which the corn was about 10 inches tall. The procedure followed by the skunk was to travel at a canter until prey was located (usually between 3 and 10 yards), turn toward the prey (frequently at right angles to the former direction of travel), make one or two bounds, and pounce on the prey in a manner similar to that of a domestic cat. The skunk apparently trapped the prey beneath its front feet. The prey was eaten immediately.

The point from which the above observations were made was too distant to observe the prey with 7 × 50 binoculars, and subsequent examination of the area did not reveal the identity of the prey species. Dr. Milton W. Sanderson, Illinois Natural History Survey, informed me that several carabid beetles occupy this type of habitat and are active during the early morning hours. The apparent relish exhibited by skunks for carabids suggests that the skunk probably was feeding on these beetles.

On June 24, 1962, between 1955 and 2040 hours, another skunk was observed while it fed in a field in which hay had been cut and raked into windrows. The procedure followed by this skunk was slightly different from the one described above: it walked slowly along one of the windrows, its movements flushing grasshoppers which flew a few feet before lighting. When a grasshopper lit in the space between the windrows, the skunk made two or three bounds and captured the insect between its forepaws.

Striped skunks frequently left evidence of feeding activities, in the form of excavations in soil, torn-open microtine runways, and overturned dried droppings of cattle. Typical sign left by skunks digging for grubs is shown in Figure 10.

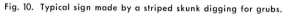

Fig. 10. Typical sign made by a striped skunk digging for grubs.

The only detectable damage caused by striped skunks on the Shannon Study Area was a result of their feeding activities. In May, 1960, a field which had been in hay crops for several years was plowed and planted to corn. There had been considerable bluegrass in the field, particularly near one field border. When the corn was 3-4 inches tall, nearly every plant in the three rows adjacent to this field border was excavated by skunks. Apparently, grubs which had been feeding on roots of the bluegrass were attracted to roots of the corn plants, and skunks excavated the corn in attempts to capture grubs.

DEFECATION

In captivity almost all striped skunks defecated in the corners of their nest boxes, opposite the entrances. Two dens of wild skunks, which I excavated, contained tunnels packed with skunk droppings. These tunnels were branches off the main tunnel of the den. Another den, known to have been occupied by skunks, had a small pile of weathered droppings near its entrance. Although droppings of skunks were collected at locations several hundred yards from the nearest den occupied by skunks, there appeared to be a strong tendency for skunks to defecate in or near den sites. This tendency has been reported for other mustelids (Cahalane 1947:183).

MATING

Wight (1931:42-47) described in detail the mating behavior of a pair of captive striped skunks. In general, his descriptions were confirmed by my observations of captive skunks in northwestern Illinois, but there were some minor variations in behavior among individuals. Briefly, the general mating behavior was as follows:

When a female striped skunk in estrus was introduced into a cage with a male, he approached her from the rear and smelled and licked her vulva. If the female was receptive, she usually bent her tail acutely to one side and straightened her hind legs. The male moved to the side of the female, grasped her by the skin of her neck with his teeth and clasped her abdomen with his front feet. The male used one of his hind feet to scratch the female's vulva. After this titillation, and alternately with titillation, the male made rapid copulatory movements until intromission was achieved. The female was completely passive until intromission and made no movements except to lower the anterior part of her body to the floor of the cage. At intromission, the female often attempted to bite the male, but these attempts were usually weak and unsuccessful. Copulatory movements were terminated following several vigorous pelvic thrusts, after which the male attempted to turn the female on her side. Although none of the males which I observed accomplished this, Wight (1931:45) reported that the male he observed succeeded in turning the female on her side before coition was completed. Separation usually occurred about 1 minute after completion of the vigorous pelvic thrusts. After separation, the male usually thoroughly licked his genital region; the female did not clean herself. Each acted indifferently toward the other. Mating attempts with females in estrus were not accompanied by vocalization by either male or female.

Wight (1931:43) commented on the nearly simultaneous occurrence of parturition among female skunks when six females were kept in a cage with each male. It was noted that captive male skunks in northwestern Illinois which had successfully bred one female immediately attempted to mount another female, but exhibited little interest in the first female for several hours. In view of the relatively large number of female skunks often residing in the same winter den with a single male in the wild (Allen 1939:218), this mating behavior appears to have a high survival value by insuring that all females are bred. It may also help to explain Wight's observation.

Seton (1926:350) found that bred females chased males away. Captive females which were bred usually fought viciously with males attempting to mount. This behavior usually began within a week after the first mating and was frequently used as a criterion of successful mating, before uterine swellings were evident. Such fights usually were accompanied by nearly continuous vocal noises and foot stamping by the female. Unbred females not in estrus usually did not fight with males attempting to mount but did not exhibit a receptive pose.

PARTURITION

Approximately 1 week prior to parturition captive female skunks became unusually defensive. Even the slightest noise outside the nest boxes was sufficient provocation to cause them to rush from the nest boxes into the adjoining cages and to stamp their front feet and make hissing noises. These gestures increased in intensity after females had given birth to their young; they frequently attempted to bite the attendant.

Before the young were born, females usually removed from their nest boxes nearly all the straw provided for nesting material. Removal of straw from nest boxes was one indication that parturition was imminent. The newly born young were permitted to lie on the wooden floors of the nest boxes. Shadle (1956:113) reported that he observed a female fashioning a nest of shredded newspapers within 2 hours after giving birth to her litter. Wight (1931:46) reported that a female began carrying nesting material 17 days before her litter was born. Natal dens of two wild skunks were excavated while they contained

Fig. 11. A female striped skunk carrying one of her young.

young; the young in one den were about 6 days old and those in the other den were about 40 days old. No nesting material was found in the first den; the second den had about a half bushel of dried stems and leaves of grasses. Apparently, very young skunks may become entangled in nesting material and thereby be prevented from nursing.

Shadle (1956:112-113) recorded the behavior of a female striped skunk during the time that two of its three young were born. One young was expelled almost instantaneously, but the head and shoulders of the other protruded from the vaginal opening of the female for several minutes prior to expulsion.

Birth of one young to a captive female skunk was observed during this study. In this instance, the pregnant female was accidentally flushed from her nest box into the adjoining cage where she arched her back and almost explosively expelled the young. The female picked up the young while it was still covered by the embryonic membranes and carried it into the nest box. Further disturbance of the female was avoided.

After the young were born, a female usually carried one of the young into the adjoining cage when the nest box was opened. The method used by females to carry their young is shown in Figure 11. Throughout the period of lactation, adult females continued to defecate in one corner of the nest boxes; the young were always clean, dry, and free of excreta.

Burns (1953:210) stated that female skunks at first nurse their young by sprawling over them, but, as the young become older, the female lies on her side. The positions assumed by the females while their young were nursing were difficult to observe because the females left their nest boxes when the boxes were opened. Most females appeared to lie on their sides; however, one female usually lay on her back with her hind feet against one side of the nest box while her young nursed.

ADOPTION AND KIDNAPPING OF YOUNG

On July 1, 1960, two juvenile males about 7 weeks old were captured by hand and placed on one side of a divided cage. On July 8, 1960, these juveniles were found to have entered the other side of the cage through a small hole in the divider. A lactating female in the other half of the cage permitted the two orphaned young to nurse with members of her own litter.

On June 11, 1961, a young female skunk about 5 weeks old was placed in a cage containing an adult female and her litter of 4-week-old young. The adult female ran into the cage from the adjoining nest box, picked up the orphaned young, and carried it into the nest box. The adult female permitted the orphaned young to nurse with members of her own litter.

Jones (1914:106) reported that barren females kept in the same pen with females nursing young will attempt to kidnap the young. As all my captives were kept in separate cages, I did not have an opportunity to observe this behavior.

Whether adoption or kidnapping of the young occurs among wild striped skunks is not known.

WEANING

Seton (1926:356) stated that striped skunks in the wild are weaned about the first of August (about 2½ months old). Schwartz and Schwartz (1959:305) reported that weaning was complete when young skunks were about 2 months old. Allen (1939:222) stated: "It is evident that these young skunks were capable of living independently of the mother by July 17. The teeth were well developed, and the animals appeared too large and vigorous to have been nourished solely by nursing a 4-pound mother. From their appearance and behavior, it is probable that in this locality young born in early May are weaned by July."

Exact time of weaning among captive striped skunks was impossible to determine because females never exhibited any aggressive behavior toward their young. When about 6 weeks old, young skunks began to eat semisolid food and could subsist without supplementary nursing when about 2 months old. However, one female permitted her young to nurse until they were nearly 4 months old; they were then placed in separate cages. Young skunks in the wild may cease to nurse when they are able to maintain themselves on solid food; therefore, weaning may not be actively controlled by adult females.

FAMILY RELATIONSHIPS

Adult females apparently did not tolerate adult males near them after the breeding season. Seton (1926:354) stated that adult male skunks were the greatest menace to the young. Thus, it appeared that adult males had no position in the family and that the family was composed only of the adult female and her young.

Young striped skunks are reported to begin accompanying their mothers on hunting trips when they are about 2 months old, and family ties are maintained until autumn (Cahalane 1947:214, Burt 1946: 149, Schwartz and Schwartz 1959:305). Although, in northwestern Illinois, I did not observe young skunks accompanying their mothers, there was considerable evidence that the adult female and her young traveled as a group. It was evident that family ties were broken soon after the female began to take her young on hunting trips; by mid-August few young remained with their mothers.

On July 6, 1961, three juveniles, each about 75 days old, were caught in live traps set within an area less than 100 yards in diameter. There was also evidence that a small skunk in another trap in the same area had been aided in its escape by a larger skunk outside the trap. Presumably, the mother skunk had overturned the trap, thereby releasing her young. On July 10, 1962, juvenile skunks about 65 days old were caught in each of three consecutive traps set in a line at about 75-yard intervals. These multiple captures of juveniles in small areas were believed to represent instances of young skunks and (presumably) their mothers traveling as family groups.

On June 28, 1962, at 1815 hours, an adult female and three of her five young (41 or 42 days old) were observed at the entrance to a den. When the adult left the vicinity of the den, she was followed for about 20 yards by one of the young. The adult turned toward the young skunk, stamped her front feet, and, when the young skunk continued to follow, carried it back to the entrance to the den. These actions were performed three times before the young skunk ceased its attempts to follow its mother. At noon on June 29, 1962, the female and three young were observed lying in a thick, weedy fencerow about 250 yards from their den; at 1935 hours, within 5 minutes after the female left her position, the fencerow was searched without finding the young. During the night of June 29–30, 1962, the adult female moved very slowly through an oat field adjoining the weedy fencerow. Presumably, she moved more slowly than usual to permit her young to accompany her. On July 6, 1962, at 0800 hours, the adult female was found lying in the weedy fencerow in approximately the same location in which she had been observed previously, but her young were not with her. On July 20, 1962, one of the young was captured in a live trap set about ½ mile from the point where the family was last observed. It appeared that some young skunks began to travel with their mothers as early as 42 days of age and became independent of parental care as early as 50 days of age.

Six of nine juvenile skunks radio-tracked during August and September spent the daylight hours in grass waterways in cornfields, and, at least during the daylight hours, were not accompanied by other skunks. On nine occasions during these months, juvenile skunks were seen at night and only once were two skunks observed traveling in company. Most striped skunks probably became completely independent of family ties about the time they were 3 months old.

Chapter V

ACTIVITY AND MOVEMENTS

ACTIVITY

Seasonal

Striped skunks in the northern portion of their range apparently remain more or less inactive for extended periods during winter (Hamilton 1937, Selko 1938a, Jones 1939, Terres 1940). Davis (1951:19) believed that striped skunks in Texas were active throughout the year, possibly more active in winter than in summer.

Hamilton (1937:326), Jones (1939:255), and Selko (1938a:320) referred to periods of inactivity of striped skunks in winter as "hibernation," but Davis (1951:19) stated that striped skunks do not exhibit characteristics of true hibernation. Folk (1963:704) defined hibernation in mammals as "a state of dormancy associated with reduced heart rate, respiration, body temperature, and total metabolism." In northwestern Illinois, rectal temperatures of seven captive striped skunks housed in outdoor cages averaged 96.3° F when the ambient temperature was 22° F, and 96.1° F when the ambient temperature was 40° F. Ellis and Barlow (1925:56) reported that rectal temperatures of skunks were about 37.5° C (99.5° F) when the ambient temperature was about 25° C (77° F). These data indicate that there is no reduction in the rate of metabolism corresponding to lowering of the ambient temperature, hence no true hibernation of striped skunks.

Several attempts have been made to correlate periods of inactivity of skunks with environmental temperature. Selko (1938a:321-322) observed no sign of skunk activity in the vicinity of 11 dens in Iowa in

January and February, 1937, when mean monthly temperatures for the 2 months were 1.7° F and 9.1° F, respectively. Observations at 12 dens during the same months in 1938, when mean monthly temperatures were about 10° F higher, revealed no sign of activity in January, but skunks were active throughout most of February. Terres (1940:217) recorded a captive skunk as "hibernating" when the average temperature was as high as 40° F. Jones (1939:256) believed that below-freezing temperatures reduced, but did not prevent, activity of skunks. Smith (1931:78) believed that there was no close correlation between temperature and resumption of activity by skunks in spring. He postulated that depth of snow cover might influence the activity of skunks. Hamilton (1937:326) found that males were active at lower temperatures than females, but that low temperatures did not prevent skunks from being active, particularly during their breeding season.

Irregular observations conducted during February and March, 1960, at a series of dens in the walls of a pit from which sand had been excavated revealed that skunks were active on 7 of 23 nights. The average minimum temperature of seven nights on which skunks were active was 12.5° F, and on nights when skunks did not leave their dens the average minimum temperature was 15.3° F. There were no significant differences between numbers of nights on which skunks were active when minimum temperatures were above and below 15° F ($X^2 = 0.759$, df = 1). Depth of accumulated snow ranged between 0 and 12 inches during the period when observations were conducted, and at least 2 inches of snow covered the ground on 21 of the 23 nights. Snow cover on nights when skunks were active ranged between 5 and 10 inches. Den entrances at which these observations were made were atypical of most skunk dens in agricultural areas of northwestern Illinois, because the den openings were in a nearly vertical bank and were protected by a few small trees from being covered by drifted snow. On the Shannon Study Area most dens were in fencerows and were usually covered by 1 to 3 feet of drifted snow, frequently for 2 to 3 weeks after snow in open areas of fields had melted. Skunks appeared to have been trapped in these dens by the crusted snow.

In early spring, 1959 and 1960, 43 striped skunks were caught in 5,036 trap-nights in traps set in road culverts. Numbers of skunks caught per trap-night in each of seven minimum daily temperature classes of 5° F each, between 25° F and 59° F, were not significantly different ($X^2 = 5.709$, df = 6).

Although there was much evidence that skunks remained inactive for extended periods during winter, there was little evidence that a single environmental factor such as temperature or depth of snow cover was wholly responsible for initiating and maintaining periods of inactivity or for stimulating resumption of activity. A combination of factors such as temperature, snow cover, crusted snow over dens, rapid changes in temperature, hunger, and sexual urges probably determined the times and duration of periods of inactivity.

Fig. 12. Percent of hourly radio-observations between 1800 and 0700 hours during August, September, and October, during which juvenile striped skunks were active. Numbers above abscissa indicate observations during each period.

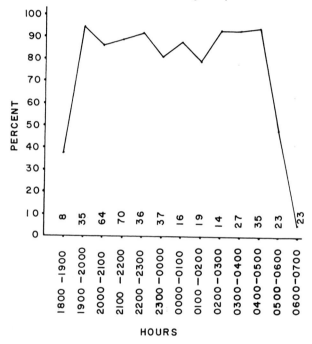

Daily

Striped skunks usually were active primarily at night, although they were observed occasionally during the daylight hours of early morning or late evening. Apparently, little is known concerning activity of skunks at night. The radio-tracking system used to determine movements of striped skunks was also used to detect whether striped skunks were active or inactive (Verts 1963a:338-339).

During August, September, and October, juvenile striped skunks apparently became active between 1800 and 1900 hours, remained active throughout the night, and returned to their dens or resting areas between 0500 and 0600 hours (Fig. 12). Of 353 radio-observations made between 1900 and 0500 hours, juvenile skunks were active on 313 (88.8 percent) occasions. No discernible peaks of activity were noted; when skunks left their dens they usually did not return until shortly before dawn. Activity of juvenile skunks did not appear to be affected by rain or strong winds, but on very cold nights during October skunks occasionally retired to their dens after being active for 2 to 4 hours.

One lactating female skunk with a litter of seven young was radio-tracked continuously throughout the hours of darkness for six nights, and for shorter periods on nine other nights. This skunk usually left

Fig. 13. Activity periods of a lactating female striped skunk with a litter of seven young. Thin lines indicate periods of radio-observation; thick lines indicate periods of activity.

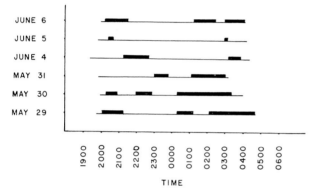

her den for two or three periods of 1 to 4 hours each during the night (Fig. 13). Although there was no definite pattern of activity, the skunk was frequently active for a short period soon after dark and for a longer period beginning a little before daylight and lasting until after sunrise. There was a trend toward longer periods of activity as the young became older.

An adult male radio-tracked between March 29 and May 2, 1962, invariably left his den within an hour after dark and returned to the den within an hour before daylight.

MOVEMENTS

Data concerning movements of striped skunks were acquired by tracking in snow, by marking and recapturing individual animals, and by use of radio-tracking equipment (Cochran and Lord 1963, Verts 1963a).

Concepts Concerning Movements of Animals

Seton (1909:26) stated: "No wild animal roams at random over the country; each has a home-region, even if it has not an actual home." Subsequently, the terms "home range" and "territory" were used to describe areas to which individual animals limit their travels. Burt (1943:346-351) distinguished between territory and home range and clarified the concepts by defining their limits. His definition of home range has been widely accepted, but some authors have modified it for use with their data (Brown 1956:54). Burt (1943:351) cautioned that areas calculated from records obtained by repeated trapping of individual animals were no more than indices to actual sizes of the home ranges but that, for a given species, the necessary "living room" was probably within definable limits.

Attempts to obtain precise indices of the true areas have resulted in several methods of calculating home ranges from linear measurements of trap-revealed movements. These are the minimum-area method, the inclusive and exclusive boundary-strip methods, the observed and adjusted range-length methods, and the probability-of-capture method. Brown (1956:54-57) discussed these methods and the criticisms directed to each.

In using trap-revealed movements to calculate home ranges certain assumptions are necessary: that the home range is fixed in time and space, that trapping does not greatly influence subsequent movements of individual animals, that individual animals caught sufficient numbers of times to apply methods of calculating area are truly representative of the species being investigated, and that the periodic presence of the investigator does not interfere with normal activities of the animals. In many cases, some or all of these assumptions are probably invalid.

Basically, movements of animals are functions of those animals and their environment. Within the broad limits of the physical capabilities of an animal, environment, life history events, and individual differences in behavior will determine how much or how little an animal will move about in search of its necessities of life. Scott (1943:442) found that red foxes "became increasingly conservative in the extent of their movements as the time for birth of the young approached." Allen and Shapton (1942:67) found that striped skunks were "traveling widely" in February and implied that sexual activity at that season might be a factor. Verts (1963b:127) found that movements of opossums were considerably greater on an intensively cultivated area than those reported for the species in wooded or partly wooded areas, and believed that the movements were more extensive because the necessi-

Table 7. Life history events which appeared to be important factors influencing movements of striped skunks in northwestern Illinois, and approximate times of the year that these events occurred.

	APPROXIMATE DATES*	
NAME OF PERIOD	MALES	FEMALES
Growth–Fattening	July 15–Dec. 1	July 15–Dec. 1
Winter Denning	Dec. 1–Mar. 15	Dec. 1–Mar. 15
Breeding	Feb. 20–Mar. 15	Feb. 20–Mar. 15
Pregnancy	–	Feb. 20–May 31
Lactation	–	May 1–July 15
Postbreeding Recovery	Apr. 1–Dec. 1	July 1–Dec. 1

* Overlap in dates may be caused by lack of synchronism among individuals or by year-to-year differences in environmental conditions.

ties of life were less abundant on the cultivated area.

Thus, it appears appropriate to discuss movements of striped skunks in relation to life history events and to environmental factors, which apparently influence the extent of movements. Events which appeared to be important factors influencing the extent of movements of striped skunks in northwestern Illinois, and approximate times of the year that these events occurred, are listed in Table 7.

Calculation of Home Range

Because of the unique characteristics of data obtained by use of radio-tracking equipment, the methods described for calculating home ranges from data obtained by livetrapping did not appear to be applicable. Attempts were made to calculate home ranges of striped skunks from records of radio-tracking by the minimum-area method and by the range-length methods. Results of these calculations were inconsistent and, in terms of actual movements of striped skunks, not descriptive. Therefore, calculations of areas of home ranges were believed inadvisable at that time.

Quantitative analyses of the movements of animals can be made without calculating areas of home ranges. Distances traveled from the home or primary den or from a calculated center of activity (Hayne 1949:7-8) may reveal as much (perhaps more) about the responses of an animal to its environment as the calculated area of its home range.

Movements of Striped Skunks

Movements of Juveniles in Late Summer and Autumn

Most juvenile striped skunks appeared to be independent by about the first week of August, when most were about 2½ to 3 months old. Food (primarily insects) was abundant and young skunks made rapid gains in weight. Accumulation of sufficient fat to sustain the young skunks during the coming winter appeared to be the most important activity during late summer and autumn.

More information concerning movements of striped skunks was ob-

Fig. 14. The percent frequency of distances between points of capture for juvenile striped skunks caught two or more times each, and the percent frequency of distances between randomly selected pairs of points obtained by radio-tracking.

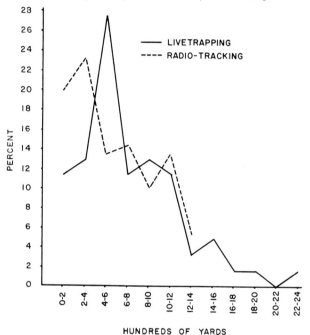

HUNDREDS OF YARDS

tained from juveniles in late summer and autumn than from skunks of any other age group at any other season. Eighty-two juveniles were captured in live traps during this season; of these, 28 were caught two or more times each. Maximum elapsed time between first and last captures of any individual was 60 days. Nine juveniles were radio-tracked for periods varying from 10 to 29 days. The radio-positions of these nine skunks were determined 457 times; 343 of the 457 determinations were made while the skunks were moving.

Of the 28 juveniles caught two or more times each, 22 were caught two times each; three, three times each; one, four times; one, five times; and one, six times. Distances between points of capture ranged from 0 to 2,210 yards and averaged 698.8 yards. The percent frequency of distances between points of capture is shown in Figure 14. Data obtained by radio-tracking were compared with those acquired by livetrapping to determine the relationship of distances between points of capture to actual distances moved by skunks. Thirty measurements of the movements of each of three skunks were made by randomly selecting pairs of points from radio-tracking data. The percent frequency of the distances between the pairs of points is shown in Figure 14. There was a significant difference between the means of these two groups of measurements ($P < 0.01$). The relatively low percentage of records of trap-revealed movements between 0 and 400 yards and the relatively large percentage between 400 and 600 yards were probably reflections of distances between traps. Live traps were frequently set at intervals of 220 and 440 yards. Hayne (1950:39) found that distances between traps and calculated sizes of home ranges of *Microtus* were positively correlated.

The percent frequency of radio-positions of nine juvenile skunks at various distances from their centers of activity are shown in Figure 15. Of 343 radio-positions, 322 (93.9 percent) were within 875 yards of the centers of activity. Brown (1956:55) pointed out that there was not an equal probability of an animal being captured at equal distances from its center of activity. Stumpf and Mohr (1962:149-154) found that the home ranges of many species tended to be longer than broad; thus the probability of an animal occurring at equal distances from its center of activity would not be equal in all directions. The above measurements, therefore, are not synonymous with radii of home ranges.

Movements of striped skunks of all ages usually occurred within an arc of 180 degrees of the dens occupied by the skunks. Of 132 locations of striped skunks obtained by radiotelemetry during periods when each of four skunks was using a single den, 94.7 percent occurred on one side of a line drawn through the point representing the home den and perpendicular to a line drawn through this point and the calculated center of activity (Fig. 16). Seventy-two percent of the locations occurred within an arc of 90 degrees. Skunks which did not live in ground dens showed a similar tendency for movement in relation to their daytime resting sites. However, it was more difficult to measure their nighttime movement patterns in relation to their daytime resting sites because their daytime resting places were not always at exactly the same points.

When juvenile striped skunks left their dens or daytime resting places, they usually traveled directly to their hunting grounds, frequently by the same routes for several consecutive nights. Figure 17 shows the positions of two juvenile skunks, obtained at random times by radiotelemetry between 2000 and 0500 hours. This time span usu-

Fig. 15. The percent frequency of radio-positions of nine juvenile striped skunks at various distances from their centers of activity.

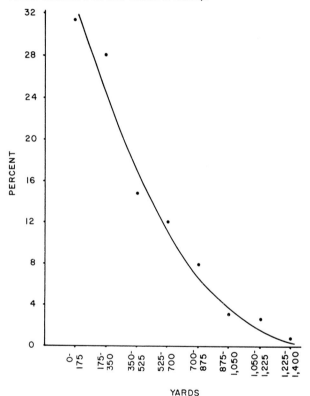

ally eliminated the positions obtained while the skunks were enroute to and from their hunting grounds. In these examples, approximately 80 percent of the positions obtained during the hours given were between 350 and 875 yards, and between 175 and 525 yards, from the dens of a 5-month-old skunk and a 2½-month-old skunk, respectively. Skunks which abandoned one den and began to use another den, or those which used two or more dens in irregular sequence during the periods that they were radio-tracked, usually continued to use the same hunting

grounds but approached them from different (sometimes nearly opposite) directions. Directions of movements of two skunks, each of which
used two different dens during the periods that they were radio-tracked,
are shown in Figure 18. Although the centers of activity were not in

Fig. 16. A diagram of the combined radio-locations of four striped skunks. Diagram was
constructed by matching points, representing home dens, with lines from these points
through the calculated centers of activity.

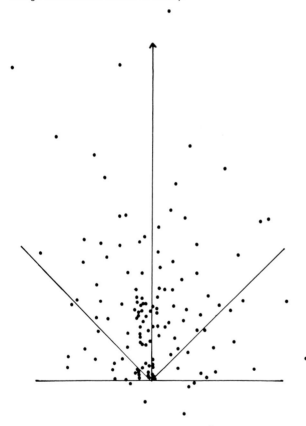

the same places, there appeared to be a strong attraction to specific
hunting grounds.

From these observations, locations of preferred hunting grounds in
relation to the locations of suitable dens or daytime resting areas appeared to be important factors in determining direction and extent of

movements of juvenile striped skunks. Such factors were probably more important than any behavior complex inherent in the species in determining characteristics of movements.

Trapping and handling appeared to affect subsequent movements of

Fig. 17. Radio-locations of two juvenile striped skunks obtained between 2000 and 0500 hours, indicating that hunting grounds were remote from home dens. Distance between arcs represents 175 yards.

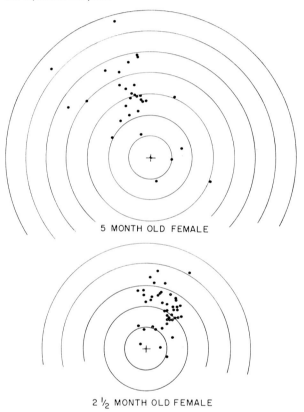

5 MONTH OLD FEMALE

2 ½ MONTH OLD FEMALE

some juvenile skunks; other juveniles appeared to be affected very little or not at all. Figure 19 shows the movements of a juvenile female, and Figure 20 those of a juvenile male, before and after being caught (second captures). Movements of the female did not appear to be greatly influenced by trapping and handling, but the male appeared to avoid the vicinity of traps in which it was captured. Of the nine juvenile skunks radio-tracked, subsequent movements of six appeared to be affected by trapping and handling. Three of six did not approach closer than 800 yards to the points of capture during the periods that they were radio-tracked. No differences in postcapture behavior between sexes were detected.

Fig. 18. The directions of movements of two striped skunks each of which used two different dens but continued to use the same general hunting areas. O represents home dens; X represents calculated centers of activity.

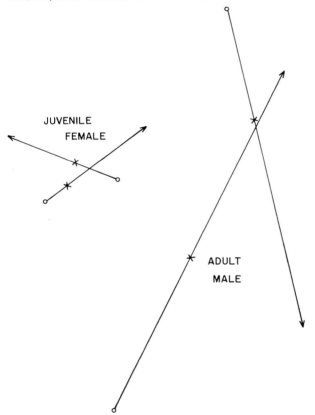

JUVENILE
FEMALE

ADULT
MALE

Movements of Striped Skunks in Winter

In northwestern Illinois, striped skunks commonly remained in their dens, except for periods of unseasonably warm weather, from about mid-December until about the first week in March. Allen (1939:226) believed that female striped skunks remained "holed up" in winter but that males made periodic sorties above ground.

During winter in northwestern Illinois, dens were frequently covered with several inches of snow (often with a thick crust), which may have prevented skunks from leaving their dens even on warmer nights. Such conditions were particularly evident on the Shannon Study Area and on other intensively cultivated areas. Most dens in these areas were in fencerows where drifting snow was trapped by the fence and by vegetation near the fence. In brushy and wooded areas, drifting of snow

Fig. 19. Radio-locations of a juvenile female striped skunk before and after recapture, indicating that subsequent movements were not greatly influenced by trapping and handling.

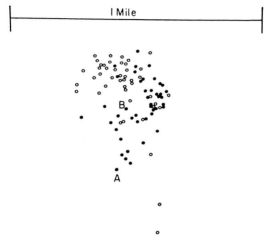

A- Released 1945, July 31,1962

• Radio-positions 2030, July 31,1962 – 2325, August 6,1962

B-Recaptured between 2325, August 6 –0050, August 7, 1962

○ Radio-positions 2015, August 7,1962 – 2100, August 18,1962

was reduced, and dens were more frequently located on acute slopes. Dens in this type of cover were more often free of snow in winter than dens in open areas.

On the Shannon Study Area, tracks of striped skunks in snow were followed on three occasions. On December 31, 1959, after a snowfall of about 1 inch, the movements of one skunk were traced through the entire course of its wanderings (Fig. 21). The most distant point from the den at which tracks were observed was 780 yards. On December 11, 1961, tracks of a skunk were followed for approximately 2¼ miles but were obscured by drifting snow before the den from which the skunk emerged or the den to which it retired were found. The ends of the trail were about 2,290 yards apart when the tracks were obscured. On March 30, 1962, tracks of two skunks emerged from the same den, but because large patches of ground were free of snow it was impossible to follow the trails of the skunks through their entire courses. The greatest distance from the den at which tracks were observed was 820 yards. The location of the patches of snow made it impossible for the

Fig. 20. Radio-locations of a juvenile male striped skunk before and after recapture, indicating that subsequent movements were influenced by trapping and handling.

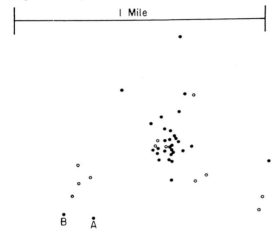

A— Released 1945, August 15, 1962

• Radio-positions 2015, August 15, 1962 – 2245, August 21, 1962

○ Radio-positions 0320, August 22, 1962 – 2015, August 25, 1962

B—Recaptured between 1930 – 2015, August 22, 1962

skunks to have traveled farther from the den without leaving detectable evidence of having done so. At least one of the skunks returned to the den from which it emerged.

On December 8, 1961, a miniature radio transmitter was attached to a juvenile female skunk, and the skunk was permitted to return to the den from which it was caught. The skunk had not left the den by December 11, at which time the entrance of the den was covered with more than 2 feet of drifted snow. The signal of the radio transmitter was checked at irregular intervals, and movements of the skunk within the den were detected until January 2, 1962. Although the transmitter continued to operate, no subsequent movements were detected. On March 8, 1962, snow above the den was removed and the den partially excavated in an attempt to recapture the skunk. Tracks in fresh snow the next day indicated that two skunks had left the den during the preceding night. When the den was completely excavated, the transmitter which had been attached to the juvenile skunk was found. The covering of the transmitter was slightly worn, indicating that the transmitter

Fig. 21. Movements of a striped skunk during a single night in winter, as determined from tracks in snow, December 31, 1959.

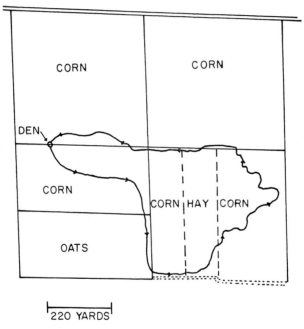

had been attached to the skunk for some time. It is certain that this female (and the other skunk in the den) did not leave the den between December 11, 1961, and March 8, 1962, a period of 87 days.

At irregular intervals between February 3 and April 5, 1960, steel traps were placed in entrances of skunk dens located in a pit from which sand had been excavated. Four skunks (three females and one male) were captured at this site between February 5 and March 25, 1960. Evidence of movements was easily detected during this period because snow completely covered the ground at all times. No evidence of movements outside the pit (about 25 yards across) was noted between February 3 and March 22, 1960.

Although these data are limited, and in some cases somewhat circumstantial, movements of striped skunks in winter appear to be confined to short excursions on warm nights. In most cases, movements were so restricted that there was little opportunity for contact between individuals occupying neighboring dens.

Movements During the Breeding Season

Calculated dates of breeding, based on development of embryos in wild pregnant female skunks, indicated that in northwestern Illinois nearly all females were bred between February 21 and March 14. The mean breeding date was March 5.

Because the breeding season was short, and the trapping conditions difficult, as usual at this season, little direct information concerning movements during the breeding season was acquired. The data presented in the preceding section indicate that movements were probably restricted, except on warm nights when there was little snow cover. Allen and Shapton (1942:66-67) trailed several skunks by tracks in snow on February 28, 1940. The greatest straight-line distances that tracks of five skunks were observed from points of emergence were "approximately a mile," 1½ miles, "about three-fourths of a mile," 1⅛ miles, and "about 600 yards." They believed that "sexual urges" were contributory to these relatively extensive movements.

The restricted breeding period indicates that the onset of the breeding season probably is independent of year-to-year differences in weather conditions. Mating of males and females occupying the same dens probably occurred in years when movements were limited by unfavorable weather. Although extensive movements possibly occurred in years when weather conditions were relatively mild during the breeding season, it appeared that breeding success was not dependent on unrestricted mobility.

Movements of Adult Males After the Breeding Season

The physical condition of male skunks appeared to be at or near the annual low point in March (Table 3). Many of the preferred foods of skunks were scarce; insects were essentially unavailable. As farmland was prepared for the forthcoming planting season, cover in the fields was destroyed, and small mammals appeared to become concentrated in the cover of the narrow fencerows. Skunks apparently took advantage of this situation as they hunted intensively along fencerows, and small mammals were food items frequently encountered in skunk stomachs. Recovery of weight lost during winter appeared to be the most important change in male skunks during the postbreeding season.

Two adult male skunks were radio-tracked during this season, one for 35 days, the other for 8 days. On March 29, 1962, one male was caught in a live trap set in the entrance to a den. When released at 1230 hours, the skunk traveled south about ⅜ mile and entered a ground den, where he stayed during the remaining daylight hours. Between 2000 hours, March 29, and 0230 hours, March 30, the skunk traveled about 2½ miles south-southwest and entered a small barn. Between March 30 and April 23, the skunk spent the daylight hours under the floor of the barn. During this period, the skunk was radio-located 49 times while it was moving (Fig. 22). Forty-three (87.7 percent) of the 49 radio-locations were within 1 mile of the barn; the greatest concentration of locations was between ½ and ¾ mile from the barn. On April 24, 1962, the skunk spent the daylight hours beneath a corn-crib about 1⅜ miles from the barn. Although the skunk was not followed every night between April 24 and May 2, the general pattern of movements of the skunk appeared to be nearly alternate use of the two retreats, with no appreciable change in the feeding area (Fig. 18).

The other male skunk radio-tracked during the postbreeding season was captured by night-lighting (Labisky 1959:1-11) on April 24, 1962, and held in a live trap until the next day. When released, the skunk traveled about 200 yards and entered a hole beneath a pile of rocks. During the night of April 25-26, the skunk moved about ¾ mile south and, thereafter, used a large brush pile as a daytime retreat. Nightly movements were predominately to the south; the skunk never went more than 200 yards in the direction of the point where it was captured. Periodic malfunctioning of the radio transmitter, topographic features, and absence of roads for the vehicle used for radio-tracking prevented determination of the exact extent of this animal's movements, but the skunk usually traveled about ¾ mile to its feeding area.

Movements of adult males after the breeding season averaged about ¼ to ½ mile greater in extent than those of juvenile males in autumn. Relative scarcity of food, and possible searches for unbred females, may account, in part, for these differences. Although no direct information was available, it was possible that movements of males decreased in extent as the abundance of food increased during late spring and summer. Very few adult males were caught in late spring and summer; perhaps limited movements were partly responsible for infrequent capture of males at these seasons.

Movements of Pregnant Females

Very little direct information concerning movements of pregnant female striped skunks was available in the literature. Jones (1950:22) caught an adult female in northeastern Kansas three times between March 31 and April 8, and calculated a minimum home range of 12.0

Fig. 22. Movements of an adult male skunk after the breeding season, March 31–April 23, 1962. Distance between arcs represents 440 yards.

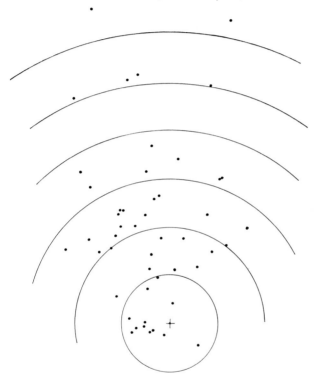

acres. Although he did not describe the reproductive status of this specimen, most female skunks in northwestern Illinois were pregnant at this season.

As the time for giving birth approached, pregnant female skunks became more difficult to capture. Of 17 pregnant females caught, only one was within 10 days of parturition. Females heavy with young probably moved no farther than ¼ mile from their dens.

Movements of Lactating Females

In northwestern Illinois, female striped skunks usually gave birth to their litters during the first 3 weeks of May; possibly a few litters were born during the last few days of April. The period of lactation and parental care usually lasted about 60 to 75 days.

On May 23, 1962, an adult female and her litter of seven were caught by excavating their den. A radio-transmitter was attached to the adult, and the young were marked by removing a toe from one front foot of each. The skunks were returned to the den after it had been reconstructed. Movements of the lactating female were followed by use of radio-tracking equipment for 44 days; the young were between 6 and 50 days old during this period.

The adult female did not leave the den during the night of May 23-24, but between 2130 hours, May 24, and 0300 hours, May 25, she moved her young to another den 350 yards from the reconstructed den. Between May 25 and June 2, the movements of the female were followed without further disturbing her or her den. During this time, the female was not absent from the den for more than 3½ hours at any time; the average period of absence was 72 minutes. At no time did the skunk travel farther than 360 yards from her den; most movements were confined to a strip about 100 yards wide and 250 yards long at the edge of a small creek.

Between June 2 and July 6, the skunk and her dens were disturbed on seven occasions. Her movements were probably influenced by these disturbances, but as the young became older the adult was absent from her den for longer periods, and her movements were more extensive than formerly. By June 12, the female was away from the den during most of the hours of darkness; the extent of her trips frequently exceeded ½ mile.

Records of Movements over Extended Periods of Time

Records of distances moved by six striped skunks, with more than 60

Table 8. *Records of distances moved by striped skunks, with more than 60 days between observations, northwestern Illinois, 1959–62.*

Sex	Age When Marked	Days Between Observations	Distance Traveled	Remarks
Female	Juvenile	411	660 yards	Recaptured, had litter
Female	Juvenile	369	1,050 yards	Recaptured, had litter
Female	Juvenile	103	1,310 yards	Found dead
Male	Juvenile	187	2,010 yards	Recaptured
Male	Adult	209	1,270 yards	Found dead
Male	Adult	848	6 miles	Recaptured

days between observations, are shown in Table 8. These data indicated that many skunks spent large portions of their lives within relatively small areas. Records of movements obtained by radio-tracking indicated that striped skunks commonly moved greater distances in a single night at some seasons than most of the distances recorded in Table 8.

Chapter VI

DENS AND DENNING

The origin, location, conformation, and relative abundance of dens used by striped skunks and associated species are aids to the understanding of the interrelationships between skunks and their environment. On the Shannon Study Area, the ecology of dens appeared to be as dynamic as that of the mammals using them. Dens were constructed, abandoned, appropriated for use by other species, remodeled, destroyed, and reconstructed. Dens used for wintering by one species might be remodeled and used as natal dens by other species. What was merely the work of a badger in securing a meal might, with small modifications, serve as a natal den for striped skunks. Dens located in hayfields, habitable by one of several species, might become nonexistent overnight when the hayfields were plowed and the land prepared for row crops.

ORIGINS OF DENS USED BY STRIPED SKUNKS

Selko (1938*b*:456-461) observed 27 ground dens used by striped skunks in Iowa and was able to determine that fourteen had been dug by woodchucks, four by badgers, four by striped skunks, and three by red foxes. Allen and Shapton (1942:60) believed that most of the 36 dens which they excavated on a study area in Michigan had been dug by woodchucks. Jones (1950:16-17) believed that dens permanently used by striped skunks in northeastern Kansas had been dug by woodchucks. On the Shannon Study Area, a single woodchuck was caught and one

other woodchuck was seen in the 4 years that investigations were conducted there. Woodchucks did not appear to be abundant anywhere
in northwestern Illinois; only 21 were captured by all methods between
1958 and 1962. Because woodchucks were scarce in northwestern Illinois, they probably did not construct many of the dens used by striped
skunks. Of 100 dens found in the Shannon Study Area, the origins of
69 were determined from signs (tracks, hair, claw marks, and shape
and size of the hole). Of these, 50 (72.5 percent) were dug by badgers,
12 (17.4 percent) by red foxes, 5 (7.3 percent) by striped skunks, and
2 (2.9 percent) by muskrats. Of the 25 dens known to have been used
by striped skunks, 11 (44.0 percent) were dug by badgers, 5 (20.0 percent) by striped skunks, 4 (16.0 percent) by red foxes, and 2 (8.0 percent) by muskrats; 3 (12.0 percent) were of unknown origins.

Badgers dug many holes about 2-3 feet deep in attempts to capture
ground squirrels (Fig. 23). Skunks frequently modified these holes for
their own use. These dens often could be detected by finding the old
ground squirrel tunnel in the wall of the larger den. A diagram of a
den of this type, used as a natal den by a female striped skunk, is shown
in Figure 24.

Dens constructed by muskrats and used by striped skunks had entrances formed by collapse of portions of the tunnels remote from the
water. These cave-ins were usually caused by the feet of livestock.

TOPOGRAPHY AT DEN SITES

Selko (1938b:455-460) found that most dens used by striped skunks
which he observed in Iowa were in hilly or rolling land. Allen and
Shapton (1942:60) reported that most dens on their study area in
Michigan were on slopes. In a survey of dens in Clay and Boone counties, Iowa, Scott and Selko (1939:97) found that most dens used by
skunks were on slopes of 5 to 10 percent or greater. The average slope
at all den sites on the Shannon Study Area was 6.3 percent, and was
5.3 percent at dens known to have been used by striped skunks. The
topography of the Shannon Study Area is gently rolling, with elevations
between 820 and 1,000 feet above sea level. Seventy-two percent of the
dens used by skunks were located between 900 and 960 feet above sea
level, but only 52 percent of the area was between these elevations.
Chi-square tests indicated that the distribution of dens was significantly
different from an expected uniform distribution on the basis of elevation ($P < 0.01$). Slopes appeared to be preferred den sites, rather than

crests or valleys; this preference probably reflected the importance of good drainage.

Fig. 23. Hole dug by badger in quest of ground squirrels. Finely chopped grasses on spoil is portion of the ground squirrel nesting material. Holes of this type were modified by striped skunks for their own use.

COVER AT DEN SITES

Selko (1938*b*:463) found that vegetative cover at most den sites was predominately bluegrass (*Poa pratensis*),[1] greater ragweed (*Ambrosia trifida*), lesser ragweed (*Ambrosia artemisiifolia*), and hemp (*Cannabis*

---

[1] Nomenclature of plants is that of Fernald (1950).

sativa). Allen and Shapton (1942:60) found 30 of 36 dens on their study area in edges of woodlots or in patches of brush; the other 6 were in hayfields. Scott and Selko (1939:96) believed that hay and pasture land provided the most suitable den sites for striped skunks. Of 25 dens used by striped skunks on the Shannon Study Area, 15 were in grassy fencerows in which the predominate vegetation was bluegrass, fescue (*Festuca* sp.), timothy (*Phleum pratense*), and foxtail (*Setaria*

Fig. 24. Diagram of a natal den used by a female striped skunk and her litter of eight. Den was modified from a hole dug by badgers.

Part of old groundsquirrel
tunnel

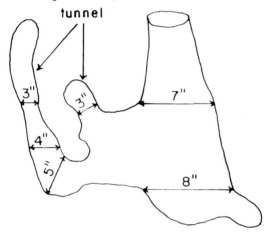

sp.) ; 8 dens were in hayfields or pastures (mostly alfalfa, *Medicago sativa*, and red clover, *Trifolium pratense*) ; and 2 dens were in weedy and brushy fencerows in which the predominate vegetation was hemp, greater ragweed, and black raspberries (*Rubus occidentalis*).

Seventy-two percent of the dens used by striped skunks had entrances directly beneath the wire of a fence (Fig. 25). These dens remained intact longer than others because they were rarely destroyed by farm equipment or trampled by livestock. Sixty-five percent of the dens not used by striped skunks also had entrances directly beneath fences.

CHARACTERISTICS OF DENS

Allen and Shapton (1942:64) found that dens which they excavated had an average of 2.19 entrances. The 30 dens observed by Selko

(1938*b*:456-461) had an average of 1.50 entrances; 16 had one entrance, 13 had two entrances, and 1 had three entrances. Of the 25 dens on the Shannon Study Area used by striped skunks, 18 had one entrance, 6 had two entrances, and 1 had three entrances, an average of 1.32 entrances per den.

Three natal dens were excavated, all of which were characterized by

Fig. 25. Den entrance located directly beneath the wire of a fence. Dens in these locations were not often destroyed by farm equipment or by the trampling of livestock. Tracks in snow at entrance of the den are those of a striped skunk.

their simplicity. None was more than 5 feet long nor had more than a single 90-degree bend in the tunnel. In two of these natal dens the young could have been reached from the surface. Dr. Thomas G. Scott told me that he had inadvertently pulled a newborn skunk from its den, along with a handful of nesting material, when he was examining dens in Iowa. Two of the natal dens excavated appeared to have been modified from holes dug by badgers when attempting to capture ground squirrels.

DENNING HABITS

Dens on the Shannon Study Area were frequently occupied by several species in succession. Of 46 dens found open in August, September, and October, 1960, 31 were occupied, or had been occupied sometime during 1961 (Table B, Appendix). Of these 31 dens, 9 were known to have been occupied by two or more species in late 1960 or in 1961. One den was known to have been occupied by two different species simultaneously. On July 10, 1959, after a heavy rain, tracks of a raccoon and a striped skunk were found leading into a den, but there was no evidence that either animal had left the den.

Seton (1926:357) reported that a single male striped skunk and as many as 20 females used the same den in winter. Allen and Shapton (1942:64) excavated five dens which contained striped skunks and found ratios of males to females of 0:1, 1:0, 1:1, 1:1, and 1:2. Allen (1939:218) excavated 11 dens which contained skunks and found the following ratios of males to females: 1:10, 1:10, 1:7, 1:1, 0:6, 0:4, 0:1, 1:0, 1:0, 1:0, and 2:0. Jones (1950:19) believed that male and female skunks used separate dens in autumn and winter in Kansas. In northwestern Illinois, three females and one male were caught in traps, set at the entrance to a den, between February 3 and March 25, 1960. No evidence that skunks had entered or left the area of the dens was found during this period. On two occasions a male and a female to which radio transmitters had been attached used the same den in autumn. In both cases, the males were young-of-the-year; thus, it is improbable that older males have harems and defend them from younger males.

After weaning, many juvenile striped skunks did not appear to use ground dens but spent the daylight hours in cornfields or grass waterways in cornfields. Whether this reflected a preference on the part of juvenile skunks or an insufficient number of dens in the vicinity of good feeding areas is unknown. After mid-September no juvenile was known to have spent the daylight hours in the open.

Chapter VII

FOOD HABITS

Food habits are one of the best documented aspects of the life history of striped skunks. Some of the important investigations of food habits of skunks are those of Lantz (1923), Dixon (1925), Hamilton (1936), Selko (1937), and Llewellyn and Uhler (1952). The rank in importance of major classes of food items, as determined by these investigators, is shown in Table 9. Most of these studies pointed out the insectivorous nature of the diets of striped skunks and the shift to diets of small mammals when insects were not available in sufficient quantities. There was some disagreement among various authors concerning importance of foods of plant origin in the diets of striped skunks.

Almost every author emphasized the apparent preference exhibited by skunks for forms detrimental to interests of man, and the relative rarity of depredations by skunks on domestic forms and game species. This was contradictory to the findings of several investigators studying the nesting success of various game species: Kalmbach (1938:614) found that skunks destroyed 30.4 percent of 351 duck nests under observation on the Lower Souris Refuge in North Dakota in 1936, but destroyed only 6.5 percent of 566 nests in 1937 after 423 skunks had been removed from the area; Kimball (1948:300) found that mammal depredations (mostly by badgers and skunks) accounted for 55.7 percent of 350 pheasant nests destroyed; Beule (1941:324) found that 4 of 25 cottontail rabbit nests under observation in Pennsylvania were destroyed by skunks; Stoddard and Komarek (1941:289) believed that skunks were responsible for the destruction of many bob-white quail nests. To my knowledge, no studies of food habits of striped skunks

Table 9. The rank in importance of major groups of food items of striped skunks, as determined by various authors.

Authority	Season	State	Number of Stomachs Analyzed	Number of Fecal Passages Analyzed	Rank of Food Items				
					1	2	3	4	5
Hamilton (1936)	Autumn–Winter	N. Y.	1,067	—	Fruits	Mammals	Insects	Grasses	Birds
Hamilton (1936)	Spring–Summer	N. Y.	30	570	Insects	Fruits	Mammals	Grain	Carrion
Llewellyn & Uhler (1952)	Autumn	Md.	47	—	Insects	Millipedes	Rodents	Plants	Birds
Llewellyn & Uhler (1952)	Winter	Md.	47	—	Insects	Rodents	Millipedes	Plants	Amphibians & Reptiles
Selko (1937)	Autumn	Iowa	—	149	Arthropods	Mammals	Birds	Vegetables	Inert
Dixon (1925)	All Year	Calif.	353	—	Insects	Grasses & Roots	Rodents	Birds	Stock

have been conducted in areas where extensive depredations of nests of game species have occurred.

Striped skunks occasionally kill and eat the young of domestic cats (Dice 1926:131), which might be considered a depredation on a domestic form.

FOOD OF STRIPED SKUNKS IN NORTHWESTERN ILLINOIS

Stomach and intestinal contents from 149 striped skunks, and 20 fecal passages, collected in northwestern Illinois were analyzed to determine food items eaten by skunks in that area. Contents of stomachs and intestines were washed out with a stream of water into a milk strainer which had a fine-mesh screen bottom. Fecal passages were softened by soaking in water for about 12 hours, carefully torn apart, and washed in running water. The washed materials were preserved in 10 percent formalin until food items were identified. Preserved materials were washed to remove the formalin, placed in shallow trays with a small amount of water, and examined with a binocular dissecting microscope. Identification of food items followed more or less standardized procedures except that insect parts were picked out, dried, and stored in coin envelopes until identified by Drs. M. W. Sanderson and H. B. Cunningham, Section of Faunistic Surveys and Insect Identification, Illinois Natural History Survey.

Because of the relatively well-verified nature of food habits of striped skunks, this investigation was not intended to be more than a survey of food items eaten by skunks in northwestern Illinois. For this reason, only frequency of occurrence of food items was recorded. It was recognized that frequency of occurrence did not provide complete information on which to base relative importance of various food items; for example, a small part of a single grasshopper in one stomach is assigned the same value as 200 grasshoppers in another stomach. Used with caution, and with a knowledge of the behavior of the species being investigated, this technique probably is sufficiently accurate to detect major trends in the diets of animals.

In their attempts to escape from traps, striped skunks usually ingested some vegetation, quantities of dirt, and other inert items around the trap site. In addition, many skunks chewed off and swallowed the portions of their feet that were inside the jaws of traps, which frequently complicated the problem of deciding whether certain items found in the contents of stomachs and intestines were ingested as food or in attempts to escape.

Food Items of Plant Origin

Hamilton (1936:240-243) stated that fruit was the most important food of skunks in New York in autumn and winter and was second in importance in spring and summer. His unusual classification of food items (Hamilton 1936:241-243, Tables 1 and 2) may be partly responsible for this conclusion because, excluding "garbage," nearly equal volumes of foods of plant and of animal origin were eaten in autumn and winter, and in spring and summer skunks ate nearly twice as much food of animal origin as food of plant origin. Llewellyn and Uhler (1952: 200) believed that 80 to 90 percent of the diets of skunks was composed of animals. Selko (1937:74), Dixon (1925:44), and Lantz (1923:9-10) provided data which tends to corroborate these conclusions. Selko (1937:74) believed that the discrepancy between his findings and those of Hamilton might be caused by differences in relative abundance of fruit-producing species.

In northwestern Illinois, the frequency of occurrence of foods of plant and of animal origin were approximately equal at all seasons (Table 10). Of the 55 identified items of plant origin eaten by striped skunks (Table C, Appendix), only corn (*Zea mays*), black cherries (*Prunus serotina*), nightshades (*Solanum nigrum* and *S. carolinense*), and ground-cherries (*Physalis heterophylla*) were believed to have been ingested as food; the remaining items were believed to have been ingested by skunks in their attempts to escape from traps. Most species of plants recorded, particularly grasses, smartweeds, and composites, were probably better indicators of habitat types in which traps were set than of an herbivorous diet of skunks.

Food Items of Animal Origin

The percent frequencies of occurrence of the most important foods of animal origin eaten by striped skunks, as determined by several authors, are shown in Table 11. Mammals and insects appeared to be the most important foods of skunks; their relative frequencies appeared to be dependent on season.

In northwestern Illinois, vertebrates occurred in a higher percentage of stomach and intestinal contents and fecal passages than invertebrates. Vertebrates, particularly mammals and birds, occurred most frequently in spring (Table 10), the season when most ground-nesting birds were laying and incubating, and when small mammals were concentrated in fencerows because their habitat was reduced by farming operations. The high percent of frequency of occurrence of striped skunk in the

Table 10. Frequency of occurrence and percent frequency of occurrence of major classes of food items from 20 fecal passages and from contents of stomachs and of intestines of 149 striped skunks, northwestern Illinois, 1959–62. Numerals in parentheses indicate numbers of analyses.

Class of Food Item	Winter (17)		Spring (67)		Summer (49)		Autumn (36)		Totals (169)	
	No.	%	No.	%	No.	%	No.	%	No.	%
Plants	14	82.4	64	95.5	44	89.8	34	94.4	156	92.3
Animals	16	94.1	62	92.5	48	98.0	35	97.2	161	95.3
Vertebrates	11	64.7	50	74.6	34	69.4	13	36.1	108	63.9
Amphibians	–	–	6	9.0	6	12.2	2	5.6	14	8.3
Birds & Eggs	2	11.8	16	23.9	6	12.2	4	11.1	28	16.6
Mammals	10	58.8	44	65.7	26	53.1	9	25.0	89	52.7
Insectivores	1	5.9	2	3.0	–	–	1	2.8	4	2.4
Rabbits	4	23.5	4	6.0	5	10.2	2	5.6	15	8.9
Rodents	7	41.2	44	65.7	23	46.9	7	19.4	81	47.9
Carnivores*	2	11.8	1	1.5	–	–	–	–	3	1.8
Artiodactyls	–	–	3	4.5	1	2.0	1	2.8	5	2.9
Unknown	–	–	1	1.5	–	–	–	–	1	0.6
Invertebrates	16	94.1	57	85.1	42	85.7	33	91.7	148	87.6
Annelids	–	–	2	3.0	–	–	1	2.8	3	1.8
Oligochaets	–	–	2	3.0	–	–	1	2.8	3	1.8
Arthropods	16	94.1	57	85.1	42	85.7	33	91.7	148	87.6
Arachnids	–	–	7	10.4	1	2.0	1	2.8	9	5.3
Insects	16	94.1	57	85.1	42	85.7	33	91.7	148	87.6
Diplopods	–	–	1	1.5	–	–	2	5.6	3	1.8
Isopods	–	–	1	1.5	–	–	–	–	1	0.6

* Exclusive of *Mephitis*.

Table 11. The percent frequencies of occurrence of the most important foods of animal origin eaten by striped skunks, as determined by various authors.

AUTHORITY	STATE	SEASON	FOOD ITEM					
			MAMMALS	INSECTS	CARRION	EARTH-WORMS	BIRDS	REPTILES & AMPHIBIANS
Hamilton (1936)	N. Y.	Autumn–Winter	24.5	25.8	14.2	4.0	2.2	2.0
Hamilton (1936)	N. Y.	Spring–Summer	21.9	57.8	2.8	–	1.8	1.5
Llewellyn & Uhler (1952)	Md.	Winter	49.0*	91.6	–	–	12.8	8.5
Llewellyn & Uhler (1952)	Md.	Autumn	23.4*	95.7	–	–	14.9	–
Selko (1937)	Iowa	Autumn	21.0	92.0†	–	–	13.0	–
Dixon (1925)	Calif.	All Year	22.6*	58.6	4.0‡	–	7.8	0.3

* Listed as rodents.
† Listed as arthropods (includes some millipedes).
‡ Listed as stock.

material analyzed (Table C, Appendix) was entirely the result of skunks grooming themselves or chewing on their feet when caught in traps. No evidence of cannibalism was noted.

Insects occurred in a large percentage of food remains examined (Table 10), and occurred most frequently in winter. This probably is misleading because of low numbers of individual insects per analysis in winter, but may also be related to a preference for insects by skunks and to the scarcity of all kinds of foods in winter. Stomachs and intestines which held greatest numbers of insects were found in late summer and early autumn.

Beetles and grasshoppers were the insects which occurred in the greatest percent of analyses (Table C, Appendix). Carabids and scarabs were the most frequently encountered beetles, possibly because of their nocturnal habits.

PREDATOR–PREY RELATIONSHIPS

The role of preference in determining the diets of striped skunks was difficult to evaluate because skunks did not cache food items, transport food to their young, or often wantonly kill prey. The tendency toward seasonal variation in diets of skunks probably indicated that availability, accessibility, and abundance of certain food items were as important as preference in determining food habits of skunks.

In the case of insects there appeared to be some adjustment in the rate of predation by skunks with the relative abundance of the prey, but in the case of small mammals the most intensive predation occurred in late winter and spring when prey populations were at or near their annual low point. Even in the latter case, it appeared doubtful that predation by striped skunks could alone impart a significant stabilizing effect on levels of prey populations, because skunk numbers were also near the annual low point at that season.

Chapter VIII

HABITATS AND POPULATIONS

HABITATS

The most descriptive statement concerning habitats of striped skunks was probably that of Bennitt and Nagel (1937:120), "there is no single, well-defined land-type that can be set apart as skunk range." Schwartz and Schwartz (1959:302-303) believed that striped skunks preferred areas where there was a mixture of woods, brushy corners, and open fields broken by wooded ravines and rocky outcrops. Burt (1948:148) and Hamilton (1943:162-163) similarly described habitats of striped skunks. Brown and Yeager (1943:471) found that the greatest harvest of skunks in Illinois occurred in rolling or bluff country where mixed farming was practiced and where there was timber and pastureland with good water resources. In a companion survey, Mohr (1943:518) believed that the highest skunk populations were in counties near the large rivers in the state, because those counties contained the most broken terrain and the most wooded land in the state.

Habitat types unsuited or poorly suited to striped skunks apparently were much easier to define than preferred habitat types. Bennitt and Nagel (1937:120) believed that the nearly complete absence of striped skunks in the Mississippi Lowland region of Missouri was due to the fact that the water table frequently rose to within 2-3 feet of the surface and made ground dens unsuitable. Certainly, less extensive areas along streams and rivers have similar conditions which probably have prevented the establishment of resident populations of striped skunks. Bennitt and Nagel (1937:120) attributed the lower populations of striped skunks in the Ozark region of Missouri to low food supply in the vast, unbroken forested areas.

The preferred habitat of a species which apparently can find the necessities of life in a wide variety of habitat types can only be determined by the relative abundance of individuals occupying each of the various habitat types. This method is a better measure of the quality or "carrying capacity" of habitat types than a measure of any predilection for certain habitats on the part of individual animals.

Fig. 26. Distribution of major woodlots on the 516-square-mile sample area in Carroll and Whiteside counties, Illinois. Stippled areas indicate woodlots.

Preferred Habitats of Striped Skunks in Northwestern Illinois

Relative populations of striped skunks in various habitats in northwestern Illinois were determined by numbers of skunks captured per unit effort in each of the various habitat types in an area of about 516 square miles in Carroll and Whiteside counties. Habitats in this area were evaluated by determining the relative quantity of woodland in each area from U.S. Geological Survey, 1:62,500 scale, topographic maps, on which the woodlots were indicated. The major woodlots on the sample area are shown in Figure 26. Although some maps used were more than 10 years old, observations made during the course of the study indicated that the extent and location of woodlots were essentially the same as those depicted on the topographic maps. A clear piece of plastic on which squares, each representing 40 acres, had been etched, was placed over each section and the numbers of squares which contained woodlots or parts of woodlots were recorded. Sections were grouped into one of five habitat classes on the basis of the number of 40-acre squares which contained woodlots. The distribution of sections, in the sample area, which contained 0, 1 to 4, 5 to 8, 9 to 12, and 13 to 16 squares with woodlots is shown in Figure 27.

Fig. 27. Distribution of sections on the 516-square-mile sample area which contained 0, 1 to 4, 5 to 8, 9 to 12, and 13 to 16 forty-acre squares with woodlots.

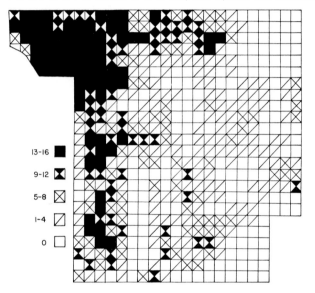

Seventy-four striped skunks were captured in 7,231 trap-nights on the area, an average of 10.2 skunks per 1,000 trap-nights. Distribution of captures (Fig. 28) was not uniform, but most captures were made in areas where the fewest woodlots occurred. More than 80 percent of the captures were made where less than one-fourth of the 40-acre squares per section contained woodlots (Table 12). Chi-square tests indicated that numbers of striped skunks caught in each habitat class were significantly different ($P < 0.01$) from the expected numbers of captures based on the total trap-nights in each habitat class.

This method of evaluating the habitat admittedly was crude because quality of woodlands was not considered. However, on other traplines

Table 12. Number and percentage of sections in each of five habitat classes, number of trap-nights, and number of striped skunks captured in each habitat class, based on the relative density of woodlots on a 516-square-mile area in Carroll and Whiteside counties, Illinois, August 1958– May 1960.

CATEGORY	NUMBER OF 40-ACRE SQUARES PER SECTION WITH WOODLOTS					TOTALS
	0	1–4	5–8	9–12	13–16	
Number of Sections	159	151	75	53	78	516
Percent of Total Sections	30.6	29.3	14.6	10.4	15.1	100.0
Number of Trap-nights Used	2,103	2,238	1,131	697	1,062	7,231
Percent of Total Trap-nights	29.2	30.8	15.6	9.7	14.7	100.0
Number of Skunks Caught	28	32	4	6	4	74
Percent of Total Caught	37.8	43.2	5.4	8.1	5.4	99.9
Skunks Caught per 1,000 Trap-nights	13.3	14.3	3.5	8.6	3.8	10.2

which were set in woodlots of at least 40 acres, but of varying quality, only five striped skunks were captured in 3,681 trap-nights.

It was evident that striped skunks resided in areas which contained considerable woodland, but in northwestern Illinois highest populations of skunks usually were found in more open country. Under certain conditions, however, woodlots appeared to be extremely important as

Fig. 28.   Distribution of striped skunk captures on the 516-square-mile sample area, 1958–60.

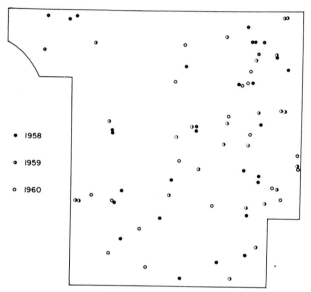

1958
1959
1960

striped skunk habitats. In February and early March, 1961, five striped skunks were caught in a woodlot of about 20 acres approximately 2 miles from the nearest other woodlot. Apparently, this woodlot provided some type of protection for skunks during winter that was not available in surrounding agricultural land.

Preferred Habitats on an Intensively Cultivated Area

A more intensive investigation of preferred habitats of striped skunks than the one reported above was conducted on the Shannon Study Area. Cultivated fields occupied more than 97 percent of the land on the study area; less than 2 percent of the land was idle and there were no woodlots. Typical scenes on the Shannon Study Area in winter and summer are shown in Figures 29 and 30.

The major crops planted on the Shannon Study Area were corn, oats, and legume and grass mixtures used for hay or pasture, or both. The acreage and the percentage of the total acreage planted to each of the major crops on the area on which skunk populations were sampled by livetrapping each year between 1959 and 1962 are listed in Table 13.

Fig. 29. A typical summer scene on the Shannon Study Area, July, 1959.

Fig. 30. A typical winter scene on the Shannon Study Area, December, 1959.

In 1959 and 1960, skunk populations were sampled by livetrapping on 6 square miles; in 1961 and 1962, livetrapping operations were conducted on only 1 square mile.

Because only 5 of 122 striped skunks captured in live traps on the Shannon Study Area were adults, the effective trapping period was considered to be July 1, when young skunks began to leave their natal dens with their mothers, to October 15, when young skunks began to restrict their movements on exceptionally cold nights. Numbers of trap-nights in the effective trapping period and numbers of striped

Table 13. Acreage and percentage of total acreage of each major crop on those parts of the Shannon Study Area on which livetrapping operations were conducted, 1959–62.

YEAR	CORN		OATS		HAY–PASTURE		FARM LOTS		IDLE GROUND		TOTAL ACRES
	ACRES	PER-CENT	ACRES	PER-CENT	ACRES	PER-CENT	ACRES	PER-CENT	ACRES	PER-CENT	
1959	1,855.3	50.6	629.1	17.1	1,090.0	29.8	54.3	1.5	40.2	1.1	3,668.9
1960	1,895.6	51.7	667.0	18.2	1,005.7	28.8	54.3	1.5	46.3	1.2	3,668.9
1961	329.0	50.8	161.5	25.0	137.6	21.2	8.4	1.3	10.8	1.6	647.3
1962	263.0	40.7	157.2	24.3	207.9	32.1	8.4	1.3	10.8	1.6	647.3

Table 14. Number of trap-nights and number of striped skunks captured in each of the major crops during the effective trapping period (July 1–October 15) on the Shannon Study Area, 1959–62.

Year	CORN		OATS		HAY–PASTURE		TOTALS	
	Trap-nights	Skunks Caught	Trap-nights	Skunks Caught	Trap-nights	Skunks Caught	Trap-nights	Skunks Caught
1959	1,707	10	1,009	3	1,365	9	4,081	22
1960	1,091	28	320	4	474	7	1,885	39
1961	3,189	27	953	4	1,170	5	5,312	36
1962	2,857	16	1,085	4	1,249	5	5,191	25
Totals	8,844	81	3,367	15	4,258	26	16,469	122

skunks caught (including those recaptured) in each of three major types of crops each year between 1959 and 1962 are listed in Table 14.

During any one year, the number of striped skunks captured in the three types of crops was not significantly different from the numbers expected on the basis of effort in each type of crop. There was, however, a significant difference ($P < 0.02$) between total numbers of skunks caught in each type of crop and the expected catch on the basis of effort in each type. Eighty-one (67.2 percent) of 122 striped skunks caught were captured in live traps set in cornfields, but traps set in cornfields accounted for only 53.6 percent of the total number of trap-nights.

Between August and November in 1961 and 1962, movements of several juvenile striped skunks were followed by means of radio-tracking equipment (Cochran and Lord 1963, Verts 1963a). Locations of skunks were recorded, while the skunks were moving, 69 and 270 times in 1961 and 1962, respectively. The number of locations in each type of crop was significantly different ($P < 0.01$) from the expected number based on the acreage of each crop on the study area. In 1962, 154 (57.1 percent) of the 270 locations occurred in cornfields, but cornfields occupied only 40.8 percent of the study area. In 1961, the percentage of radio-locations occurring in cornfields, and the percentage of the area occupied by cornfields, were approximately the same. Data on movements of one female skunk which spent most of each night for a period of about 4 weeks hunting in a hayfield on which manure had been spread may have caused this discrepancy.

The importance of cornfields as habitats for striped skunks (particularly juvenile skunks) in intensively cultivated areas was probably a result of the cover and food provided. At the time when young skunks began to forage with their mothers, the corn was usually at least 50 inches tall in northwestern Illinois. Cornfields probably provided young skunks excellent protection from both aerial and terrestrial predators and did not restrict their movements, as did the more dense crops of hay or oats. It appeared difficult for young skunks to travel through unmowed hayfields and oatfields, and upon release from live traps most skunks entered the nearest cornfield.

Cornfields, and especially fencerows bordering cornfields, appeared to be good feeding areas for skunks. Signs characteristic of those made by skunks digging for grubs and beetles were frequently observed in such sites. Red-legged grasshoppers, one of the preferred summer and autumn foods of striped skunks, were most abundant along fencerows bordering cornfields.

Although cornfields appeared to be an important component of striped skunk habitat, a continuous area of several square miles planted to corn probably would be poorer habitat for skunks than an area of similar size in which cornfields were intermixed with fields planted to other crops.

POPULATIONS

Population levels of fur-bearing mammals are frequently estimated by a variety of methods, almost all of which are based on recapturing individual animals caught and marked previously. Use of this technique requires the assumption that all animals, whether marked or unmarked, are equally susceptible to being caught in traps. Because movements of some striped skunks were apparently influenced by trapping and handling, this assumption was believed to be invalid. It was impossible to apply compensatory factors in calculating population levels of striped skunks because effects of trapping and handling could not be accurately determined. Therefore, calculations of population levels were made by conventional methods only for purposes of comparison and do not imply actual numbers of animals per unit area.

Estimates of populations of striped skunks varying from less than 2 per square mile to more than 50 per square mile have been reported. Jones (1939:225) estimated an autumn population of 31 striped skunks per square mile by trapping and removing animals from a 1⅛-square-mile study area in Pennsylvania. Scott and Selko (1939:96) estimated 1.64 and 4.04 striped skunks per square mile in Clay and Boone counties, Iowa, respectively. Their censuses were made in spring by enumeration of dens. Allen and Shapton (1942:64-65) estimated a winter population of about 12.8 skunks per square mile on a study area in

Michigan. Burt (1946:149) reported that the normal winter population of striped skunks was about 58 per square mile on good range in southern Michigan. Bennitt and Nagel (1937:120) estimated from reports of trappers and hunters that the breeding population of striped skunks in Missouri averaged about 1.9 per square mile.

Brown and Yeager (1943:471), Allen and Shapton (1942:66), and Allen (1952:137) believed that population levels of striped skunks fluctuated widely from year to year. All these authors believed that disease may be one of the most important causes of abrupt declines in numbers of skunks.

Population Indices

Several methods were used to census skunk populations during the present study. These were the capture–recapture method on the Shannon Study Area, numbers of striped skunks caught per unit effort on the sample area of about 516 square miles in Carroll and Whiteside counties, and statewide counts of skunks killed by vehicles on roads and highways in Illinois and Iowa. The latter censuses were conducted through cooperation of state police and rural mail carriers in the two states.

Populations on the Shannon Study Area

Livetrapping operations were conducted on the Shannon Study Area between 1959 and 1962 to ascertain population levels of striped skunks. During one or more of these years livetrapping was conducted in all months except January, February, and March, but because relatively few captures were made prior to July 1 or after September 30, population estimates were made for the July 1-September 30 period only. In addition, a sample of 29 striped skunks was removed from the area in October 1960, by steel trapping, after marking operations were completed in September.

Trapping effort, numbers of captures of striped skunks, and indices to striped skunk populations calculated by four methods are shown in Table 15. Indices to populations on the study area were not in complete agreement, but at least some of the discrepancies were attributable to different numbers of traps used per unit area. In 1959 and 1960, trapping procedures were essentially identical, and all indices pointed to an increase in numbers of skunks, although the degree of increase varied among the indices. In 1961, trapping effort per unit area was increased approximately sixfold, because the rate of recapture was be-

Table 15. Trapping effort, numbers of captures, and indices to population levels of striped skunks on the Shannon Study Area for the period July 1-September 30, each year, 1959-62.

YEAR	NUMBER OF TRAPS PER SQUARE MILE	NUMBER OF TRAP-NIGHTS USED	NUMBER OF SKUNKS CAPTURED	NUMBER OF SKUNKS CAUGHT PER 1,000 TRAP-NIGHTS	MEAN DISTANCE OF EACH CAPTURE TO FOUR NEAREST CAPTURES (YARDS)	NUMBER OF SKUNKS PER SQUARE MILE (CAPTURE-RECAPTURE METHOD)	NUMBER OF SKUNKS PER SQUARE MILE (PETERSON INDEX)*
1959	25	2,682	18	6.7	718.1	9	–
1960	25	2,278	39	17.1	502.8	13	18±11
1961	141	4,964	32	6.5	260.8	37	–
1962	100	4,789	23	4.8	330.1	–†	–
Totals	–	14,713	112	7.5	–	–	–

* Based on a sample of 29 skunks caught in October 1960, after marking operations were completed in September.
† Recaptures too infrequent for calculation of number per square mile.

lieved to be low, due to the relatively wide spacing of traps. Undoubtedly, the excessive number of traps used in 1961 resulted in a low number of captures per 1,000 trap-nights, and the mean distance between captures may have been reduced because of the increase in density of traps. Numbers of skunks per square mile, calculated by the capture-recapture method, were believed to represent truer indices to population levels between 1959 and 1961 than did the other methods

Fig. 31. Distribution of capture sites of 16 striped skunks caught on the Shannon Study Area, July 1–September 30, 1959, showing tendency toward clumping of captures. Only the first site of capture is shown for skunks caught more than one time each. Each square represents approximately 1 square mile.

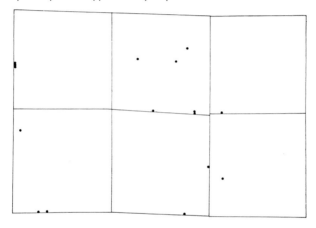

of calculating population levels. However, on the basis of observed reproduction and survival rates, the calculated increase in population on the area between 1960 and 1961 could not have occurred without ingress of skunks from adjoining lands. In 1962, recaptures of marked skunks were made too infrequently to permit calculation of populations by the capture-recapture method, even though the density of traps was four times that used in 1959 and 1960. Numbers of skunks per 1,000 trap-nights and distance between captures both indicated that the population level of striped skunks on the Shannon Study Area was lower in 1962 than in 1961. Thus, skunk populations on the Shannon Study Area were believed to be lowest in 1959, increasing in 1960, highest in 1961, and declining in 1962.

The distribution of striped skunks on the Shannon Study Area appeared to be neither uniform nor random, but clumped (Figs. 31 and 32). In 1959, when 16 different individuals were caught (Fig. 31), it was believed that the clumped distribution was the result of capturing several members of the same litter before dispersal of the young occurred. In 1960, when 29 different individuals were caught (Fig. 32), a similar clumped distribution was apparent, but because nearly twice as many skunks were captured this explanation was probably not entirely valid.

Den sites were strongly correlated with topography; thus, capture sites of young skunks would seemingly be correlated with topography

Fig. 32. Distribution of capture sites of 29 striped skunks caught on the Shannon Study Area, July 1–September 30, 1960, showing tendency toward clumping of captures. Only the first site of capture is shown for skunks caught more than one time each. Each square represents approximately 1 square mile.

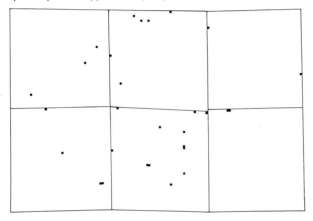

because of the restricted movements of the young. However, there were no significant differences between numbers of capture sites and expected numbers of capture sites, based on the area within each 20-foot interval of elevation between 820 and 1,000 feet above sea level ($X^2 = 8.556$, df $= 8$). Environmental differences were probably responsible for the clumped distribution of skunks, because as the population level increased the size of the occupied area increased (Figs. 31 and 32). As the population increased, striped skunks may have been forced into less desirable portions of the habitat. In times of extremely high population levels, occupied areas may fuse to form a more or less continuous population; this condition was not observed on the Shannon Study Area.

Differences between occupied and unoccupied portions of the study area, which might be responsible for the clumped distribution of striped skunks, were not ascertained. However, it was strongly suspected that the proximity of good feeding areas to den sites or to daytime resting areas may have been involved.

Population Indices Obtained with Steel Traps

Data obtained by trapping with steel traps set in road culverts were used to compare year-to-year population levels on the sample area of approximately 516 square miles in Carroll and Whiteside counties. In late summer and autumn 1958, and in spring 1959 and 1960, trapping procedures were essentially identical. In spring 1961, traps were set in road culverts in areas in which trapping success was highest during the three previous trapping periods. In spring 1962, traps were set in road culverts throughout the area, but the systematic procedure was abandoned in favor of lines of traps, which were more easily attended.

Numbers of trap-nights used to sample skunk populations, numbers of skunks caught, and numbers of skunks captured per 1,000 trap-nights each year are shown in Table 16. With the exception of 1961, when a more selective trapping procedure was employed than in other years, numbers of skunks caught per 1,000 trap-nights did not vary greatly. The slightly higher rate of capture per unit effort in 1958 was probably attributable to higher skunk populations in late summer and early autumn than in spring.

In the 5 years that trapping for striped skunks was conducted in northwestern Illinois, trapping success in some areas was consistently greater than in other areas. Areas in which skunks were more easily caught were usually 1 to 2 miles in diameter. This observation, and the great increase in numbers of striped skunks caught per unit effort in 1961 by trapping only in areas where skunks had been caught previously, supports belief that the distribution of skunks tended to be clumped.

Statewide Censuses of Skunk Populations

Two statewide censuses of furbearer populations and distributions, which included the striped skunk, were made about 25 years ago in Illinois. Brown and Yeager (1943:438-448) interviewed all fur-takers in sample strips across 10 counties which they believed were representative of the eight regions of the state. Mohr (1943:511-512) used monthly reports by trappers of furbearers to derive indices to distributions of Illinois furbearers. Brown and Yeager (1943:470) found highest populations of striped skunks in the Northwest Hills and in the River Bluffs and Bottoms. They reported wide fluctuations in numbers of skunks caught per square mile between the 2 years of the study. Mohr

Table 16. *Numbers of trap-nights, numbers of skunks captured, and numbers of skunks captured per 1,000 trap-nights in steel traps set in road culverts in Carroll and Whiteside counties, Illinois, each year, 1958–62.*

YEAR	SEASON	NUMBER OF TRAP-NIGHTS	NUMBER OF SKUNKS CAPTURED	NUMBER OF SKUNKS CAUGHT PER 1,000 TRAP-NIGHTS
1958	Summer–Autumn	2,268	31	13.7
1959	Spring	2,822	26	9.2
1960	Spring	2,300	17	7.4
1961*	Spring	472	16	34.0
1962	Spring	2,581	32	12.4
Totals		10,443	122	11.7

* Traps set only in areas where skunks had been caught previously.

(1943:518) reported a similar distribution of striped skunks in Illinois, but found that the trend between the two trapping seasons of 1929-30 and 1941-42 was toward fewer captures. He (p. 518, Fig. 9) presented a map indicating relative densities of striped skunks, by county, in Illinois.

Fur-taker reports were available for some of the intervening years between Mohr's report and the present investigation. Data derived from the more recent reports probably were not comparable with those used by Mohr, because the decline in demand for long-haired furs, accompanied by a decline in value of pelts, probably had a greater effect on numbers of striped skunks caught for fur than did changes in population levels of skunks.

In 1961, two statewide counts of striped skunks killed by vehicles on roads and highways were conducted simultaneously in Illinois. Rural mail carriers and state policemen counted all skunks observed along their routes between midnight, August 19, 1961, and midnight, August 20, 1961. They also recorded the number of miles driven and the county or counties through which they drove during that period. These counts were repeated between midnight, August 20, 1962, and midnight, August 21, 1962, in Illinois, and were extended to include Iowa.

Because numbers of striped skunks seen and numbers of miles driven in any one county were relatively small, and because many mail carriers and state policemen traveled roads in two or more counties, data were analyzed on the basis of zones in each of the two states. In Illinois, the three former conservation zones were used (Fig. 33A), and in Iowa, the nine agricultural areas were grouped into three zones, each of which extended across the state in an east-west direction (Fig. 33B).

Relative densities of striped skunks in the three zones in each of the two states, based on numbers of skunks seen per 1,000 miles driven, are shown in Tables 17 and 18.

In Illinois, numbers of striped skunks observed per 1,000 miles driven by rural mail carriers and by state policemen in 1961 were greatest in the northern zone and least in the central zone. Rural mail carriers reported seeing 2.58 times as many skunks per 1,000 miles driven in the northern zone as in the central zone, and 2.17 times as many in the

Fig. 33. Zones used in analyzing statewide counts of striped skunks, made by rural mail carriers and state policemen. (A) Illinois. (B) Iowa.

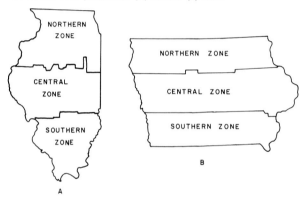

northern zone as in the southern zone. State policemen reported seeing 1.54 times as many skunks in the northern zone as in the central zone, and 1.44 times as many in the northern zone as in the southern zone.

In 1962, both rural mail carriers and state policemen reported fewer skunks per 1,000 miles driven in Illinois than in 1961. Rural mail carriers observed 2.54 times as many skunks per 1,000 miles driven in the northern zone as in the central zone, and 1.93 times as many in the northern zone as in the southern zone. State policemen observed 1.80 times as many skunks per 1,000 miles driven in the southern zone as in the northern zone, and 1.68 times as many in the southern zone as in the central zone. I am unable to suggest a satisfactory explanation for the discrepancy between relative numbers of striped skunks observed by state policemen and by rural mail carriers in the three zones in 1962. I am inclined to favor the counts made by rural mail carriers because there were nearly three times as many usable reports from them as from state policemen, and rural mail carriers in Illinois had cooperated with

Table 17. *Numbers of miles driven, numbers of striped skunks observed, and numbers of striped skunks observed per 1,000 miles driven by rural mail carriers and by state policemen in Illinois, August 20, 1961,* and August 21, 1962.†*

		RURAL MAIL CARRIERS			STATE POLICEMEN		
ZONE	YEAR	MILES DRIVEN	STRIPED SKUNKS SEEN	STRIPED SKUNKS SEEN PER 1,000 MILES DRIVEN	MILES DRIVEN	STRIPED SKUNKS SEEN	STRIPED SKUNKS SEEN PER 1,000 MILES DRIVEN
Northern	1961	20,114	172	8.55	38,341	161	4.14
	1962	23,582	171	7.25	29,994	86	2.87
Central	1961	18,358	61	3.32	20,470	55	2.68
	1962	24,506	70	2.86	20,764	44	2.12
Southern	1961	13,962	55	3.94	18,208	52	2.86
	1962	18,377	69	3.75	14,118	68	4.82
Totals	1961	52,434	288	5.49	77,019	268	3.46
	1962	66,465	310	4.66	64,876	198	3.05

* Based on 520 usable reports from state policemen and 970 usable reports from rural mail carriers.
† Based on 432 usable reports from state policemen and 1,209 usable reports from rural mail carriers.

the Illinois Natural History Survey previously by making counts of bobwhite quail, cottontail rabbits, and pheasants along roadsides.

Numbers of striped skunks observed by rural mail carriers per 1,000 miles driven in Iowa were approximately equal for the three zones

Table 18. *Numbers of miles driven, numbers of striped skunks observed, and numbers of striped skunks observed per 1,000 miles driven by rural mail carriers and by state policemen in Iowa, August 21, 1962.**

	RURAL MAIL CARRIERS			STATE POLICEMEN		
ZONE	MILES DRIVEN	STRIPED SKUNKS SEEN	STRIPED SKUNKS SEEN PER 1,000 MILES DRIVEN	MILES DRIVEN	STRIPED SKUNKS SEEN	STRIPED SKUNKS SEEN PER 1,000 MILES DRIVEN
Northern	15,143	74	4.88	6,572	35	5.33
Central	12,458	55	4.41	8,256	40	4.85
Southern	8,684	41	4.73	5,536	17	3.08
Totals	36,285	170	4.69	20,364	92	4.52

* Based on 564 usable reports from rural mail carriers and 120 usable reports from state policemen.

(Table 18). Numbers of striped skunks observed by state policemen in the northern zone of Iowa were approximately equal to numbers of striped skunks observed in the central zone, but were 1.73 times greater than numbers observed in the southern zone (Table 18).

Rural mail carriers in Iowa and Illinois observed nearly equal numbers of striped skunks per 1,000 miles driven, but state policemen in Iowa reported seeing 1.48 times as many striped skunks per 1,000 miles driven as their counterparts in Illinois (Tables 17 and 18).

Chapter IX

REPRODUCTION

One of the ways to measure the degree of success attained by a population of a given species is by evaluating reproductive capabilities of that population. An understanding of factors influencing the reproductive capabilities, and of morphological and physiological changes associated with reproduction, is essential to an understanding of other facets of the life history and of the population dynamics of that species. For these reasons, reproductive life history and morphological changes associated with reproduction, observed among striped skunks in northwestern Illinois, are described in this chapter.

FEMALE REPRODUCTIVE ORGANS

The reproductive organs of the female striped skunk consist of paired ovaries, oviducts, uterine horns, and a single vagina and urogenital sinus. Each ovary is nearly enclosed by an ostium and a heavy deposit of fat. The ostia are lateral to the ovaries and each is connected to an oviduct which is highly convoluted except at the distal end where it joins the uterine horn. The uterine horns are fused for about 8 mm (in the anestrus female) proximally to their junction with the vagina. Through this distance the two horns are separated by a septum, forming a bipartite type uterus. The vagina is joined by the urethra, forming a urogenital sinus which opens to the exterior. The presence of an os clitoris was not demonstrated.

Seasonal changes of female reproductive conditions were probably best expressed by the ovaries and uteri.

Ovaries

Leach and Conaway (1963:69-70) described the histological development of ovaries of striped skunks 3 days to 11 weeks old. They found
both monovular and polyovular follicles in ovaries from striped skunks
3 to 9 weeks old, and first observed degeneration of both types of follicles in skunks 11 weeks old.

A series of ovaries from striped skunks 5 months to 2 years old, in
various stages of the reproductive cycle, were sectioned at 10 micra

Fig. 34. Photomicrographs of ovarian section, showing changes from juvenile condition
through early pregnancy. (A) Ovarian section from a skunk about 5 months old. About
11 ×.

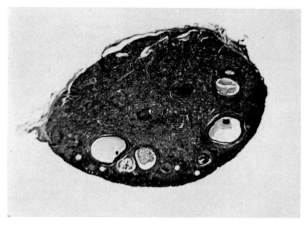

and examined under the microscope. None of these ovaries exhibited
polyovular follicles, corroborating the findings of Leach and Conaway
(1963, 72-73) that most polyovular follicles degenerated during the
first summer of life, and probably none persisted to the first breeding
season.

Juvenile female striped skunks killed in October (about 5 months
old) had ovaries which contained numerous primary follicles in the
cortex, several medium-sized follicles, and many medium-sized atretic
follicles (Fig. 34A). The largest follicles in skunks of this age caused
no bulging of the surfaces of the ovaries. There was very little interstitial tissue observed. At about 7 months of age, skunks had ovaries
which contained many primary follicles in the cortex, but there was
no increase in number or size of follicles with antra. Blood vessels in
ovaries of skunks of this age were much more numerous than in ovaries
of skunks about 5 months old.

In early February, female skunks (about 8½ months old) had follicles which caused a slight bulging of the surfaces of their ovaries. The number of primary follicles observed in the cortex was greatly increased. Ovaries exhibited an increase in vascularization. In late February, just

Fig. 34. (B) Ovarian section from a skunk about 8½ months old. About 11 ✕.

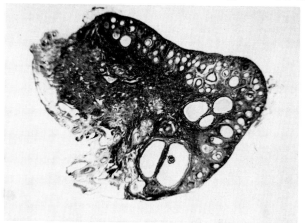

Fig. 34. (C) Ovarian section from a skunk which had recently ovulated. About 11 ✕.

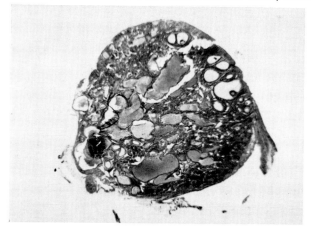

prior to estrus, the follicles were considerably enlarged and caused a pronounced bulging of the surfaces of the ovaries. There appeared to be little change in numbers of primary follicles in the cortex (Fig. 34B).

Recently ovulated follicles observed in ovaries of striped skunks killed in mid-March were filled with erythrocytes; all other large unovulated follicles appeared atretic (Fig. 34C). There were very few primary follicles in the cortex, but relatively large numbers of small follicles with antra, and a few medium-sized follicles. In early pregnancy, prior to the time that uterine swellings could be observed (hence, less than 12 days after conception), small corpora lutea were evident (Fig. 34D). There were a few small and medium-sized follicles, some of which were atretic, and a few primary follicles in the cortex.

Corpora lutea appeared to reach their maximum development approximately midway through gestation (Fig. 35A). Dawson (1941:

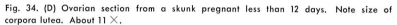

Fig. 34. (D) Ovarian section from a skunk pregnant less than 12 days. Note size of corpora lutea. About 11 ✕.

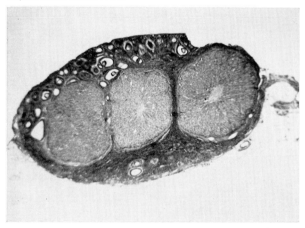

161) found that corpora lutea of pregnancy in the domestic cat, a species with essentially the same period of gestation as that of the striped skunk (Asdel 1946:167), reached maximum size between 10 and 16 days after mating. The major portion of the ovarian vascularization appeared to be in the corpora; few vessels were seen in the peripheries of the ovaries. Numbers of medium-sized and small follicles with antra appeared to be reduced. The larger follicles caused some bulging of the surfaces of the ovaries, but this probably resulted from crowding of the ovarian tissue by the corpora lutea rather than from the great size of the follicles themselves. Some reduction in the size of corpora lutea was evident after about 45 days gestation (Fig. 35B). Liche (1939:900) found that corpora lutea of pregnancy in domestic cats began to regress about 20 days after mating. Within 2-3 days after parturition the size of the corpora lutea of striped skunks

was approximately one-fourth their greatest size during pregnancy (Fig. 35C). By 90 days postpartum the corpora were barely detectable (Fig. 35D), and by 150 days postpartum only tiny scars persisted.

Fig. 35. Photomicrographs of ovarian sections showing changes from midway through pregnancy through 90 days postpartum. (A) Ovarian section from a skunk pregnant for about 30 days. About 11 ✕.

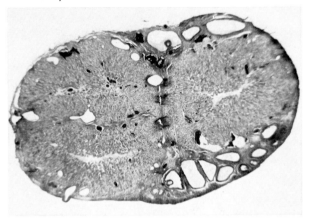

Fig. 35. (B) Ovarian section from a skunk pregnant for about 45 days. Note regression in size of corpora lutea. About 11 ✕.

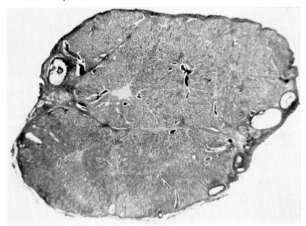

Corpora lutea were never observed in ovaries of captive females (examined by laparotomy) which failed to breed. Whether this indicates that striped skunks are induced ovulators, or that captive females which failed to breed also failed to reach breeding condition, is unknown. One nulliparous female exhibited behavior somewhat typical of pseudo-pregnancy (i.e., became vicious and aggressive) but no corpora lutea were observed in her ovaries.

Fig. 35. (C) Ovarian section from a skunk 2-3 days postpartum. Note rapid decrease in size of corpora lutea. About 11 ✕.

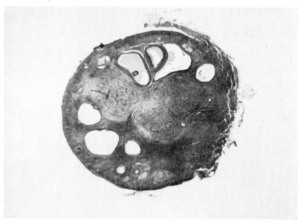

Fig. 35. (D) Ovarian section from a skunk about 90 days postpartum. About 11 ✕.

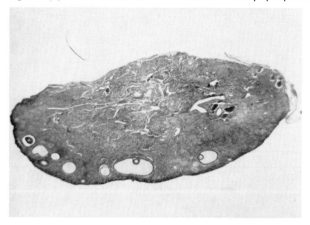

Throughout pregnancy and the period of lactation, medium-sized and large submature follicles were observed in portions of the ovaries not occupied by corpora lutea. Atretic follicles of all sizes also were observed throughout these periods. These observations may indicate that stimulation of follicles continued throughout pregnancy and lactation but that follicles so stimulated degenerated before ripening.

The large submature follicles observed during pregnancy apparently had no role in the reproductive processes, and their probable fate was atresia. Leach and Conaway (1963:72) were able to induce ovulation in juvenile striped skunks within a period of 10 days with injections of pregnant mare serum and of human chorionic gonadotropins. Thus, it appeared that large, submature follicles already present in the ovaries were not a requirement in cases similar to that recorded by Shadle (1953:388), in which a female striped skunk was successfully bred 9 days after parturition.

Fig. 36. Photomicrographs of cross sections of uteri showing changes from juvenile condition through early pregnancy. (A) Uterine section from a skunk about 5 months old. About 11 ×.

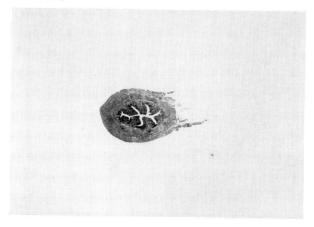

Uteri

Seasonal changes of the uteri were probably best represented by the shape and size of the uterine glands, the thickness of the endometrium, and the size and number of blood vessels in the endometrium.

The endometrium of the uterus of an anestrus juvenile striped skunk approximately 5 months old was thin and contained short, straight, narrow uterine glands which formed a radial pattern around the lumen. The lumen was irregularly shaped (nearly stellate) and contained several branches (Fig. 36A). The folds of the endometrium surrounding the lumina were rounded. The myometrium was relatively thin. Uteri of older juvenile anestrus skunks showed similar characteristics, except that the folds of the endometrium surrounding the lumina were more angular and the uterine glands were slightly longer and thicker than those of the younger juveniles; the myometrium also appeared to be slightly thicker.

The uterus of a striped skunk during proestrus appeared essentially the same as uteri of anestrus skunks, except that the uterine glands were slightly longer and thicker. Uteri of skunks at estrus had somewhat dilated uterine glands, but they remained uncoiled and extended no more than half the distance to the base of the endometrium. Dawson and Kosters (1944:28-29, Pl. 3) stated that the glands in uteri of domestic cats extended to the base of the endometrium at estrus. At

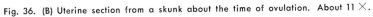

Fig. 36. (B) Uterine section from a skunk about the time of ovulation. About 11 ×.

estrus, the angular nature of folds of the endometrium in the uteri of striped skunks was pronounced (Fig. 36B).

Shortly after ovulation, glands of the endometrium were dilated but showed only a slight degree of coiling. The endometrium was thicker than that of a skunk during proestrus, but the thickness of the myometrium was essentially unchanged (Fig. 36C).

Approximately 30 days after mating, glands of the endometrium showed extensive dilation and coiling and extended to the base of the endometrium (Fig. 36D). There was no observable dentate condition of the epithelium as reported in the domestic cat by Dawson and Kosters (1944:30-31, Pl. 11). There was a slight increase in vascularization of the endometrium. Throughout pregnancy there was an increase in the coiling of the glands and in number and size of blood vessels of the endometrium (Fig. 37A).

Shortly after parturition the lumina were very narrow and had lost much of their angularity (Fig. 37B). The endometrium was considerably more dense than before parturition, because of collapse of the coiled uterine glands. About 15 days postpartum the lumina were

Fig. 36. (C) Uterine section from a skunk pregnant for less than 12 days. About 11 ×.

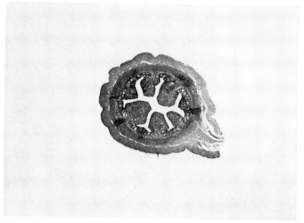

Fig. 36. (D) Uterine section from a skunk pregnant for about 30 days. About 11 ×.

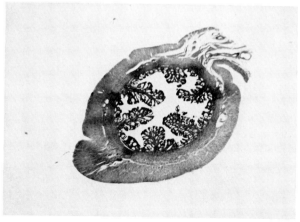

narrow and without branches. The endometrium was thin and contained a few short, uncoiled glands. Large blood vessels near the base of the endometrium were still evident. Between 30 and 75 days postpartum, the lumina became branched, and the large blood vessels of the endometrium became reduced in size and number. There were a few short, uncoiled uterine glands. A uterus collected about 90 days postpartum lacked large blood vessels in the endometrium, but had brown stains at the base of the endometrium which appeared to be hemolyzed erythrocytes (Fig. 37C). At this time, except for the brown stains and a slight dilation of the lumina, the uterus appeared essentially the same as the uteri of juvenile anestrus females.

Fig. 37. Photomicrographs of cross sections of uteri showing changes from late pregnancy through 90 days postpartum. (A) Uterine section from a skunk pregnant for about 45 days. About 11 ×.

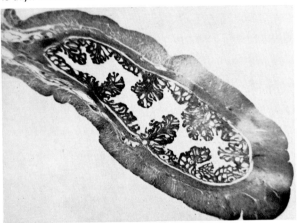

MALE REPRODUCTIVE ORGANS

The reproductive organs of the male striped skunk consist of paired scrotal testes, epididymides, and vasa deferentia, a prostate gland, and a urogenital sinus with a urethra which opens to the exterior through a somewhat fibrous penis. A thin, slightly curved os baculum is present.

Seasonal changes in the reproductive organs of male striped skunks were probably best expressed by the testes and epididymides.

Size was considered to indicate the degree of development and function of testes. Two methods of measurement were employed to evaluate relative sizes of testes of striped skunks caught at different seasons: weight (without epididymides), and an index calculated by multiplying the greatest and least equatorial diameters of testes.

The mean weight of one testis from juvenile striped skunks in August (2½ to 3½ months old) was 0.3 gram and the average of testicular indices was 62.0. Mean monthly weights and indices of testes of juveniles indicated that size of testes increased as a straight-line function of age at least until December (Fig. 38). The average size of the testes then increased at a decelerating rate until a peak was reached in March, after which the average size of testes declined (Fig. 38). Among adult males the low point in average size of testes occurred in August.

Fig. 37. (B) Uterine section from a skunk 2-3 days postpartum. About 11 ×.

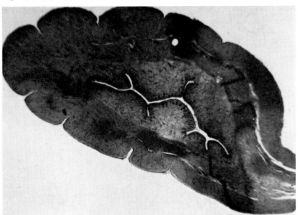

Fig. 37. (C) Uterine section from a skunk 90 days postpartum. About 10 ×.

Albert (1961:315-316) stated that spermatogenesis among "seasonal breeders" occurred only during the relatively short breeding period. Among juvenile striped skunks, spermatogenesis was first observed in the testes of a specimen killed in December, when the age of most juveniles was about 7 months. Among adults, spermatozoa were de-

tected in all months except January and September, months in which
no examinations were made. Figures 39A and 39B show the vasa
efferentia of the epididymides of a juvenile skunk collected in October
and an adult skunk collected in April, respectively. Numbers of smears

Fig. 38. Mean monthly indices of diameters of testes and mean monthly weights of testes
from striped skunks, northwestern Illinois, 1959–60. Open symbols indicate indices;
closed symbols indicate weights. Number nearest symbol is sample size. Curves were
drawn to indicate trend of indices.

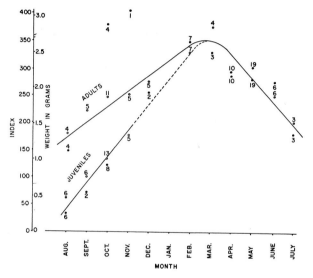

examined and numbers of smears which contained spermatozoa each
month are listed in Table 19. Whether epididymides of individual
males contained spermatozoa for most of the year was not determined.

No quantitative analyses of semen of striped skunks were conducted,
but spermatozoa usually appeared to be most abundant in smears made
from epididymides of skunks killed between February and May. Although spermatozoa were found to be present throughout the summer
months, males possibly did not have sufficient numbers of spermatozoa
in their epididymides to fertilize a female if estrus had occurred at that
season.

The histology of the testes of juvenile striped skunks in July, August,
and September was essentially the same as that of prepuberal human
testes. The histology of the testes of striped skunks older than 7 months
was essentially the same as that of adult human testes (Sohval 1958:
249-252). In July and August, seminiferous tubules of striped skunks

were more or less solid masses of undifferentiated cells and spermatogonia, but by September the beginning of lumen formation was evident. Fairly well-formed lumina were found in some seminiferous

Fig. 39. Photomicrographs of longitudinal sections of the epididymides of a juvenile and of an adult striped skunk. (A) Section of epididymis from a juvenile skunk collected in October. About 70 ✕.

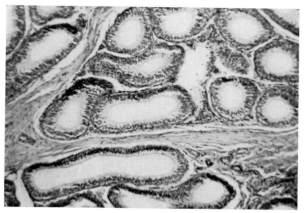

Fig. 39. (B) Section of epididymis from an adult skunk collected in April. Note vasa efferentia are packed with spermatozoa. About 70 ✕.

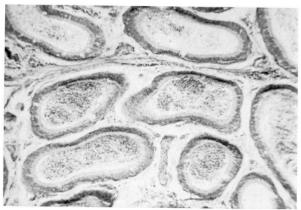

tubules of juvenile skunks killed in October (Fig. 40A), and a few spermatozoa were seen in some of the lumina of a specimen collected in December.

Among juvenile and adult striped skunks average diameters of the seminiferous tubules were about 130μ and 250μ, respectively (Figs.

Table 19. *Numbers of adult striped skunk epididymides examined, and numbers and percents of epididymides which contained spermatozoa each month, northwestern Illinois, 1959–62.*

Month	Number of Epididymides Examined	Number of Epididymides with Sperm	Percent of Epididymides with Sperm
January	0	–	–
February	7	3	42.9
March	3	3	100.0
April	11	7	63.6
May	19	15	79.0
June	6	6	100.0
July	3	1	33.3
August	3	1	33.3
September	0	–	–
October	2	1	50.0
November	1	1	100.0
December	2	1	50.0
Totals	57	39	68.5

40A and 40B). Prepuberal and adult human tubules have average diameters of about 60μ and 200μ, respectively (Sohval 1958:249). There were some seasonal changes in average diameters of seminiferous tubules among striped skunks. The average monthly diameter of seminiferous tubules reached a peak in February, then declined to a low point in August (Fig. 41). Diameters of seminiferous tubules appeared to be positively correlated with weights and diameter indices of testes (Fig. 38).

BREEDING SEASON

Striped skunks apparently breed in February or March throughout most of their range (Seton 1926:350, Wight 1931:45, Hamilton 1937: 326-327, Allen 1939:218, Allen and Shapton 1942:67, Jones 1950: 25, Davis 1951:18). Means and ranges of breeding dates of striped skunks caught in northwestern Illinois, calculated from embryonic growth, for 1960 to 1962 are shown in Table 20. These data indicated that the breeding season was restricted to a relatively short period in late February and early March, and that there was a relatively high degree of stability in mean breeding dates from year to year. Wight (1931:43) commented on the apparent synchronization of estrus among skunks in Oregon, but Hamilton (1963:123) presented data which indicated that striped skunks in New York had a wide range of breeding dates.

Seton (1926:350) claimed that female striped skunks not bred dur-

Fig. 40. Photomicrographs of longitudinal sections of the testes of a juvenile and of an adult striped skunk. (A) Section of testis from a juvenile skunk collected in October. About 70 X.

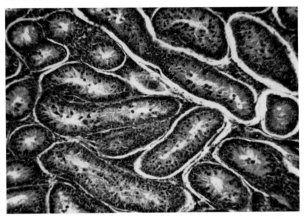

Fig. 40. (B) Section of testis from an adult skunk collected in April. About 70 X.

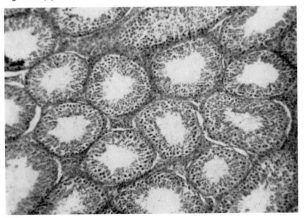

ing their first estrous cycle had a second estrous cycle about 4 weeks later. No direct evidence to corroborate or to refute this claim was obtained, but one female killed in 1960 had a calculated breeding date of March 29, 23 days later than the average breeding date of other pregnant skunks collected that year, and 31 days later than the earliest breeding date in 1960. This late breeding date possibly represents breeding during a second estrous cycle.

Seton (1926:350) stated that female skunks born the previous year bred about a month later than older females and gave birth to their litters in June, whereas older females gave birth to their litters in May. In northern Illinois, potential birth dates of skunks projected from calculated dates of conception, on the basis of a 63-day period of gesta-

Fig. 41. Mean monthly diameters of seminiferous tubules in testes of striped skunks caught in northwestern Illinois. Means were calculated from 10 diameters measured in testes from each of two skunks. Open symbols indicate juveniles; closed symbols indicate adults.

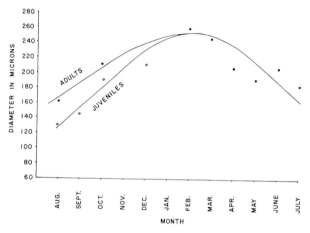

tion, for 19 gravida[1] indicated that only one litter would have been born as late as June 1. The mean calculated breeding date of 13 females born the previous year was March 7, and that of four older skunks was March 3. Allen (1939:219) presented data which he believed substantiated Seton's observation. However, he estimated ages of females by body weight, a highly variable and unreliable criterion.

Two captive females, one the 12-month-old daughter of the other, gave birth to litters 6 days apart, the older female 6 days after the younger. Both females failed to breed when placed in cages with males for 3 days beginning 30 days prior to the time they were eventually successfully bred. This observation, and observations on wild females,

---

[1] Term proposed by Snyder and Christian (1960:652) to denote the total number of embryos in a single pregnancy, hence, the antenatal counterpart of "litters."

Table 20. *Mean breeding dates and ranges of breeding dates of wild female striped skunks, northwestern Illinois, 1960–62.*

YEAR	NUMBER OF PREGNANT FEMALES EXAMINED	MEAN BREEDING DATES	RANGES OF BREEDING DATES
1960	4	March 13	Feb. 27–March 29
1961	4	March 3	Feb. 27–March 10
1962	11	March 5	Feb. 21–March 14
Totals	19	March 6	Feb. 21–March 29

tend to indicate that age of the female was not a factor influencing the date of breeding.

It appeared likely that factors other than age were important in determining breeding dates of wild female striped skunks. Immobility of male skunks, caused by deep crusted snow covering winter dens, may have influenced breeding dates of some skunks in some areas. Females cohabiting with males in winter dens were probably bred by these same males during the females' first estrous cycles. Females residing in winter dens without males may have bred during their second estrous cycles if males were unable to leave their winter dens or were prevented from entering those of females. In 1960, the deep crusted snow which covered the ground during most of February and March in northwestern Illinois may have prevented some female skunks from mating during their first estrous cycles. This may have caused the relatively wide range of breeding dates (Table 20).

In view of the behavior of striped skunks during winter and the environmental conditions to which skunks are subjected at that season in northwestern Illinois, the mechanism responsible for the synchronization of the estrous cycle is difficult to postulate. Day length, possibly modified by temperature, is frequently considered to be the external stimulus initiating onset of the breeding season of many vertebrates. In many instances female skunks were trapped in their winter dens by drifted snow for 60 days or more prior to the time that they bred; in such situations they presumably would not have been stimulated by day length. Temperatures within dens (particularly when covered by snow) should have been relatively constant.

Seton (1926:353) reported that a correspondent recorded two litters reared by one female skunk in a single year. Shadle (1953:388) reported an instance of a female breeding and giving birth to a second litter after her first litter had died because the female had failed to lactate. On September 13 and 14, 1960, two juvenile striped skunks weighing 1.1 and 0.9 pounds, respectively, were captured on the Shannon Study Area. Skunks of these weights were usually 7 or 8 weeks old. Thus, these young were born about mid-July and were conceived about the first week of May. Unless the female or females which bore these young had lost a previous litter, it is doubtful that the two captured juveniles were members of a second litter. Because a minimum of 4 months was required from conception to weaning of young, it appeared doubtful that striped skunks had time to rear two litters successfully in a single year at this latitude.

GESTATION PERIOD

Seton (1926:353) stated that the gestation period of a striped skunk was 63 days but that gestation periods as long as 72 days had been recorded. Shadle (1953:388) recorded a female striped skunk giving birth to a litter 75 days and 66 days after her first and last mating, respectively. Wight (1931:47) recorded a gestation period of 62 days in a striped skunk. Three captive females in northwestern Illinois for which exact breeding dates were known gave birth after gestation periods of 62, 62, and 66 days.

GROWTH OF EMBRYOS

Llewellyn (1953:321) measured crown-rump lengths of raccoon embryos at intervals during development and at parturition, and believed that dates of conception could be estimated from these data. Sanderson 1961b:55) measured greatest lengths of uterine swellings of pregnant raccoons and fitted a line to these data by the least-squares method. From this line he was able to estimate dates of conception with a maximum error of 4 days.

Uteri of living pregnant striped skunks whose dates of breeding were known, and whose dates of parturition were determined later, were examined by laparotomy at irregular intervals between the 6th and 59th days of gestation. No uterine swellings were observed on the 6th and 10th days of gestation. Ten measurements of diameters of uterine swellings were made between the 12th and 59th days of gestation (Fig. 42). Diameters of uterine swellings were measured because of difficulties encountered in accurately measuring crown-rump lengths and lengths of uterine swellings, particularly during early stages of pregnancy.

Analyses of the above data indicated that an excellent correlation existed between diameters of uterine swellings and duration of gestation among striped skunks ($r = + 0.959$). A line fitted to these data (Fig. 42) by the least-squares method revealed that dates of conception of

Fig. 42. Relationship between the duration of gestation and the diameter of uterine swellings in striped skunks.

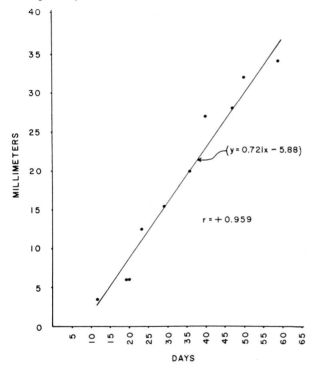

striped skunks could be estimated from diameters of uterine swellings, with a maximum error of about 5 days.

Measurements of diameters of uterine swellings containing living embryos on the 25th, 39th, 49th, and 58th days of gestation of a female striped skunk which ultimately resorbed all embryos of the gravidum did not deviate from this line by more than 4 days.

LITTER SIZES

Seton (1926:353) stated that female striped skunks bore four young in their first litter and six to eight in subsequent litters. He reported a litter of 16 recorded by a correspondent. Schwartz and Schwartz (1959: 305) stated that the sizes of striped skunk litters ranged from four to six. Davis (1951:19) reported three to seven young per litter among skunks in Texas.

Among 21 pregnant female striped skunks caught in northwestern Illinois, the number of embryos per gravidum averaged 7.33 ± 0.25 and ranged from five to nine. The average number of living embryos per gravidum was 6.33 ± 0.52 and ranged from zero to nine. Most of the difference between the mean number of embryos per gravidum and the mean number of living embryos per gravidum was caused by the death and partial resorption of two complete gravida, one of seven embryos, the other of nine embryos. No other gravidum contained more than two embryos undergoing resorption.

Among 39 female striped skunks which had given birth to litters, the mean number of placental scars was 7.15 ± 0.28 and ranged from 4 to 11. There were no significant differences between mean numbers of embryos per gravida and mean numbers of placental scars ($t = 0.480$, df $= 58$). Although there were no significant differences between the mean number of living embryos per gravidum and the mean number of placental scars ($t = 1.38$, df $= 58$), there was a 13 percent loss of embryos through resorption.

For 58 parous female striped skunks for which the sites of implantation were recorded, there were no significant differences in mean numbers of implantation sites between the two horns of the uteri ($t = 0.076$, df $= 114$).

Only one striped skunk had placental scars which could be divided into groups on the basis of degree of pigmentation. Of 15 placental scars on the uterine horns of this skunk, 9 were faded and 6 were deeply pigmented. It was believed that these groups of placental scars represented different litters.

PREVALENCE OF PAROUS FEMALES

Of 75 adult female striped skunks captured between April 1 and December 31, 72 (96.0 percent) were parous. These data indicated that female striped skunks in northwestern Illinois rarely failed to breed.

Chapter X

SEX RATIOS AND AGE RATIOS

SEX RATIOS

Few data pertaining to sex ratios of striped skunks, and few data from which sex ratios of striped skunks can be calculated, have been recorded. Bennitt and Nagel (1937:120) reported a sex ratio of nearly 1:1.4 in favor of males for 760 striped skunks caught by trappers in Missouri. Hamilton (1937:326, Table 1) reported the sex of 259 and 153 striped skunks caught by trappers in New York during the winters of 1931–32 and 1933–34, respectively. Sex ratios calculated from his data were 1:1.3 and 1:2.6 in favor of males for the two winters, respectively. He attributed the differences in the two sex ratios to differences in activity of the two sexes in relation to temperature. Jones (1950:26) reported a sex ratio of 1:1.6 in favor of males among striped skunks in northeastern Kansas. Hamilton (1963:124) reported the sex ratio of 34 embryonic skunks as 1:1.27 in favor of males. Sex was recorded for specimens in several other studies of striped skunks, but the limited number of specimens recorded in each study made calculation of sex ratios for the species in other areas impractical.

Sex Ratios Among Striped Skunks in Northwestern Illinois

In northwestern Illinois, sex was recorded for 395 individual striped skunks caught in traps between 1959 and 1962, 216 males and 179 females. Sex ratios were calculated for various segments of this sample which were obtained by different methods, and for embryos and for young skunks born in captivity. In this report, all sex ratios are expressed as numbers of males per female. Chi-square was the statistical test used to determine if the ratios deviated significantly from an expected 1:1 ratio. Chi-square in $r \times 2$ contingency tables (Steel and Torrie 1960:370) was used to test for differences in male:female composition of samples between years. For a discussion and example of this method see Edwards (1962:126-127).

The sex ratio of 78 embryonic striped skunks (sex distinguishable by the position of the genital papilla after about 35 days gestation) in 11 gravida collected between 1960 and 1962 was exactly 1:1. Differences in sex ratios of embryos between years were not significant ($X^2 = 1.84$, df = 2). The sex ratio of 24 striped skunks born in captivity was 1:1.7; not significantly different from the expected 1:1 ratio ($X^2 = 1.50$, df = 1). The sex ratio of 84 juveniles caught in live traps was 1:0.8; not significantly different from an expected 1:1 ratio ($X^2 = 0.76$, df = 1). Although year-to-year differences in sex ratios among this group were evident (Table 21), the differences were not significant ($X^2 = 0.65$, df = 3). Among 144 adults caught in steel traps set in road culverts between April and October, the sex ratio was 1:1.3. This ratio was not significantly different from an expected 1:1 ratio ($X^2 = 2.78$, df = 1). There were significant differences ($P < 0.01$) among sex ratios of this group of adults between years. In 1958 and 1959, sex ratios were significantly in favor of males ($P < 0.05$), but in 1961 and 1962, although not significant, sex ratios were decidedly in favor of females (Table 21). The magnitude of change (Fig. 43) indicated a definite shift in the sex ratio of the population. Because males ap-

Table 21. Numbers of males and of females, and sex ratios of juvenile and of adult striped skunks caught each year, northwestern Illinois, 1958–62.

	Juveniles*				Adults†			
Year	Num- ber of Males	Number of Females	Total	Sex Ratio (Males per Female)	Num- ber of Males	Number of Females	Total	Sex Ratio (Males per Female)
1958	–	–	–	–	18	6	24	1 : 3.0
1959	10	10	20	1 : 1.0	23	11	34	1 : 2.1
1960	11	16	27	1 : 0.7	12	7	19	1 : 1.7
1961	9	12	21	1 : 0.8	7	10	17	1 : 0.7
1962	8	8	16	1 : 1.0	22	28	50	1 : 0.8
Totals	38	46	84	1 : 0.8	82	62	144	1 : 1.3

* Caught in live traps between July 1 and September 30.
† Caught in steel traps set in road culverts between April 1 and October 31.

peared to travel more widely than females at all seasons (thus, would be expected to come within the radii of attraction of baited traps more frequently), sex ratios of samples only slightly in favor of females may not have indicated the true magnitude of the discrepancy.

Fig. 43. Percent female striped skunks among samples of adults caught in steel traps, April–October, and among juveniles caught in live traps, July–September, northwestern Illinois, 1958–62.

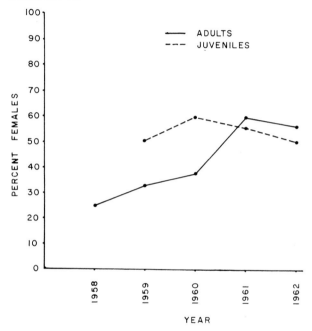

Causes of Changes of Sex Ratios

Any significant deviation from the theoretical 1:1 sex ratio among a sample of mammals may be explained on the basis of:

1. Sampling bias due to differences in behavior of the two sexes, or to selectivity by the sampling technique;

2. Differential mortality between sexes;

3. Unknown causes.

Also, the same reasons may be used to explain differences in sex ratios from year to year, even though the sex ratios for any or all years for which samples were collected were not significantly different from 1:1.

Although unknown causes are probably the most frequently offered explanation for a deviation from a 1:1 sex ratio, sampling bias is probably the most frequent actual cause. If sampling techniques were uniform, the degree of bias in samples should have remained relatively uniform among striped skunks from year to year. Assuming that the sampling technique was not a cause of bias, significant differences in sex ratios among striped skunks in northwestern Illinois between years must have been a result of differential mortality between sexes.

Changes in year-to-year sex ratios among striped skunks in northwestern Illinois may have been related to differences in rates of mortality among males of different ages. Among juveniles in 1959 and 1960, there was a trend toward fewer males, and among adults between 1958 and 1961, there was a significant shift ($P < 0.05$) toward a higher proportion of females (Table 21). These data tend to indicate that the differential in mortality occurred during the juvenile period.

Survival of females during winter possibly was enhanced by the reduction of the total population, caused by the losses among males. This, and the polygamous mating behavior exhibited by skunks, may explain the gradual increase in population level observed among striped skunks on the Shannon Study Area between 1959 and 1961.

AGE RATIOS

Few data pertaining to age ratios among populations of striped skunks have been recorded. Schwartz and Schwartz (1959:301) reported that striped skunks may live as long as 10 years in captivity. Among captives for which I have records, the oldest was still alive 63 months after it was captured as a 2-month-old juvenile; several of my captives attained an age of 3 years.

In the wild, few striped skunks attained even one-third of their potential 10-year life-span. Linduska (1947:128) reported that among 115 striped skunks marked in Michigan none was known to have lived longer than 2 years. The oldest marked skunk recaptured in northwestern Illinois was estimated to be at least 42 months old. These short life-spans indicated that mortality rates were relatively high and that complete replacement of the population occurred relatively rapidly.

Methods for Determining Ages of Striped Skunks

No single criterion was found to be satisfactory for determining ages of striped skunks. Schwartz and Schwartz (1959:301) suggested using the length of the os baculum to distinguish male skunks less than 1 year old from older males, and length, diameter, and color of teats to distinguish females which had bred from younger females. In males less than 1 year old they found the os baculum to be less than ¾ inch long, and about ⅞ inch long in older males. The epiphyseal cartilages of the radii and ulnae were ossified in only four of nine males from northwestern Illinois which had ossa bacula ¾ inch or less in length. In 2 of 24 males which had ossa bacula more than ¾ inch long the epiphyses were not ossified. Thus, the two criteria gave conflicting results for 18.2 percent of the animals to which they were applied.

Changes associated with bearing and rearing young appeared to be good criteria for distinguishing between adult and juvenile females. Of 37 adult female striped skunks examined between April and July, when juveniles could be separated from adults by size alone, all were pregnant or lactating.

It was possible to determine ages of striped skunks within narrower limits than were provided by these methods by using a combination of several criteria. The most important of these were determination of the whelping season in the areas from which skunks were collected, closure of epiphyses, and dry weights of the lenses of eyes.

In northwestern Illinois, most female striped skunks were bred in late February or early March and gave birth to their litters in May. A sample of skunks collected in any month contained animals in age groups approximately 1 year apart. For example, a skunk collected in northwestern Illinois in October would be either 5 months old, 17 months old, 29 months old, or older in steps of 12 months. Other criteria for determining ages of skunks were of little value without knowledge of the month in which most striped skunks in a given area were born.

Only 2 of 52 striped skunks captured between January and May had epiphyses which were not ossified; one was collected in January, the other in March. Apparently, ossification of the epiphyses was completed at about 8 to 9 months of age. In summer and autumn, striped skunks which were young-of-the-year could be distinguished from older skunks by this criterion alone.

Dry weights of the lenses of the eyes have been used as criteria of age in several species of mammals and birds (Lord 1959, 1961, 1962; Sanderson 1961c; Kolenosky and Miller 1962; Beale 1962; Payne 1961; Campbell and Tomlinson 1962; Dahlgren et al. 1964; Roseberry and Verts 1963). The dry weights of lenses of eyes of striped skunks also appeared to increase with age. Lenses of male striped skunks appeared to be slightly heavier than those of females of the same age; for this reason lens weights of the two sexes were analyzed separately.

The distribution by month of the means of the dry weights of both lenses of striped skunks caught between January 1960 and August 1962 tended to fall into three fairly well-defined groups (Figs. 44 and 45). The group with the lightest lenses were skunks with unossified epiphyses

Fig. 44. Monthly distribution of lens weights of 84 female striped skunks, northwestern Illinois, 1960–62. Closed symbols represent lens weights of skunks which had unossified epiphyses.

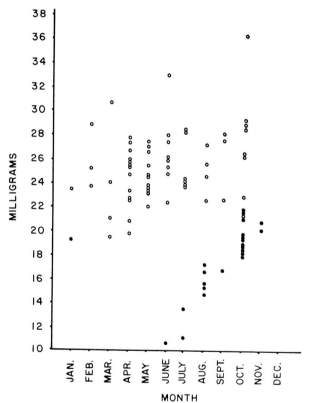

and represented animals in their first calendar year of life. The group with the next heaviest lenses had ossified epiphyses and were believed to represent animals in their second calendar year of life. Two females tagged as juveniles and recaptured as adults in October (hence about 17 months old when killed) had average lens weights in this group. The group with the heaviest lenses were believed to represent animals in their third calendar year of life or older. A captive male 718 days old had an average lens weight in this group (34.1 mg).

By using a combination of lens weights, closure of the epiphyses, and the month in which skunks were born, it was possible to determine the ages of striped skunks within limits of 1 month to 19 months. Skunks older than 19 months could be distinguished from younger animals, but the year of their birth was difficult to estimate.

Fig. 45. Monthly distribution of lens weights of 76 male striped skunks, northwestern Illinois, 1960–62. Closed symbols represent lens weights of skunks which had unossified epiphyses.

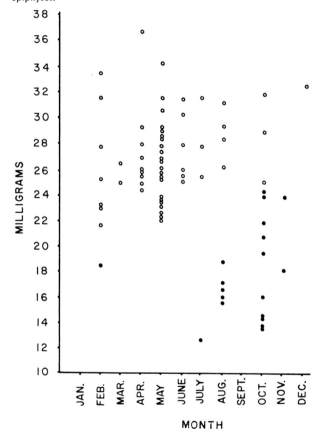

Age Ratios and Rates of Mortality Among Striped Skunks in Northwestern Illinois

Ages of 154 striped skunks caught in steel traps in northwestern Illinois between December 30, 1959, and August 31, 1962, were estimated by the techniques described previously. Each skunk was assigned to a

Table 22. Numbers of striped skunks in each yearly age-class in a sample of 154 caught in northwestern Illinois, December 30, 1959–August 21, 1962; and age distribution in a population of skunks, based on the age distribution and reproductive rate among 1,000 adult skunks. (The latter should not be interpreted as a life table for striped skunks.)

AGE IN YEARS	NUMBER OF SKUNKS CAUGHT	IN A STABLE POPULATION*		
		NUMBER OF SKUNKS PER 1,000 ADULT SKUNKS	NUMBER OF SKUNKS DYING DURING YEAR	PROBABILITY OF DYING DURING YEAR
0–1	70	3,038†	2,291	0.754
1–2	65	747	529	0.708
2–3	19	218	183	0.840
3–4	3	35	35	1.000
4+	0	0	0	0.0

* Population indices indicated an increase in numbers between 1960 and 1962.
† Based on a 1:1 sex ratio among adults, 96.0 percent parous females, and an average of 6.33 young per litter.

yearly age-class (Table 22); lens weight was used to estimate ages of skunks older than 19 months, although admittedly the estimates were crude.

Data presented in Table 22 (*column 2*) were not representative of age ratios of striped skunks in northwestern Illinois; far fewer juveniles occurred in the sample than were expected to occur on the basis of the calculated reproductive rate. Young skunks usually did not leave their natal dens until nearly 2 months old and did not travel as widely as older skunks for several weeks after they became independent. Such behavior reduced the probability of capturing young animals in traps in the same ratio as they occurred in the population. This discrepancy was circumvented by considering the distribution of adult skunks (those over 1 year old) in different age-classes in the sample as representative of the distribution of adults in different age-classes of the population, and the juvenile segment was determined by applying the average annual reproductive rate to the adult segment (an arbitrary 1,000 animals) of the population (Table 22, *column 3*). From these data, numbers of deaths (Table 22, *column 4*) and the probability of dying during any year (Table 22, *column 5*) were calculated.

The above calculations required the assumption that the population was stable between 1960 and 1962; all population indices indicated that an increase in numbers actually occurred. Survival rates calculated from yearly age ratios of adults indicated that a decline in numbers occurred between 1960 and 1962.

Quick (1963:192) warned that data obtained from animals caught in traps were not as reliable for calculating rates of mortality as those obtained from records of natural deaths. Apparently, little confidence can be placed in age ratios and mortality rates of striped skunks caught in traps. Some factors involved in discrepancies described in these analyses may be: sampling error due to sample bias, errors in determining age, year-to-year fluctuations in numbers of striped skunks, unequal trapping effort within the period of sampling, and differential selectivity of trapping due to increased wariness of older animals.

Although calculated mortality rates of striped skunks were considered to be unreliable, it was evident from the short life-span and high reproductive rate that mortality, particularly among juveniles, was high. Probably less than 35 percent of the striped skunks born attained 1 year of age.

Causes of Mortality Among Striped Skunks in Northwestern Illinois

Although the rate of mortality was undoubtedly high, it was difficult to determine the causes of death and the relative mortality caused by each factor. However, the few recorded causes of death that were obtained constitute a basis for understanding the high mortality rate in a species with such a specialized and highly effective system of defense.

Predation

Great horned owls, mountain lions, eagles, coyotes, badgers, foxes, and bobcats are among wild species known to prey occasionally on striped skunks (Bent 1938:307, Cahalane 1947:215, Young and Jackson 1951: 148-149, Hall 1955:211, Young 1958:74, 93). All these authors pointed out that predator species were usually near starvation when they resorted to preying on striped skunks.

No direct evidence of predation on striped skunks was noted in northwestern Illinois, although red foxes, badgers, and great horned owls were common in the area. Indirect evidence of avian predation on a striped skunk occurred in the form of large patches of hair adhering to resinous gum about 6 feet above the ground in a black cherry tree. Because striped skunks are unable to climb trees (Seton 1926:318), occurrence of skunk hair in this location possibly indicated that an avian predator carried a skunk to the site. A great horned owl which often roosted in a tree about ¼ mile from the site was the suspected predator, but no skunk remains were found in several regurgitated pellets beneath its roost.

Although most domestic dogs avoid striped skunks after an initial encounter with one of them, a few dogs apparently become persistent skunk killers. Two dogs belonging to farmers on the Shannon Study Area were reported to have such tendencies.

Pest Control

Striped skunks were considered to be pests by many persons residing in northwestern Illinois because of their habit of defending themselves with their musk when startled or when attacked by dogs. Skunks which chose to live in farm buildings because numerous rats and mice were available there may have constituted a hazard, but many objections to skunks arose through ignorance of their habits and behavior. Nevertheless, many farmers waged a relentless attack on skunks by shooting, "gassing," and trapping, without regard to where the skunks lived. Three of 14 skunks known to have died on the Shannon Study Area were shot by farmers; several others were reported to have been shot but their carcasses were not found. No dens were known to have been "gassed" on the Shannon Study Area but several farmers repeatedly threatened to do so.

Insecticides

It has become more or less common knowledge that some chlorinated hydrocarbon insecticides used for field control of injurious insects may be highly toxic to certain species of mammals. In discussing the effects of one of these poisons (dieldrin), Scott *et al.* (1959:423) reported that differential vulnerability to poisoning among various wild mammals seemed to result from "characteristic behavior and the degree of inherent resistance to the poison." They believed that species which were primarily terrestrial and included insects in their diets were particularly vulnerable to poisoning. Striped skunks are included in this group of species.

Although use of chlorinated hydrocarbon insecticides by farmers in northwestern Illinois increased during the period of study, no direct evidence of mortality among striped skunks, resulting from these poisons, was acquired. Unusual behavior exhibited by several skunks suspected of having rabies but whose tissues did not contain viruses of the disease may have been due to intoxication resulting from ingestion of poisons of this type.

Diseases

Mortality among striped skunks resulting from diseases was usually difficult to detect; specific diseases must have caused a far greater number of deaths than was indicated by the numbers of carcasses found. Many skunks suffering from fatal diseases probably died in their dens or in other places where their carcasses were concealed. The probability of finding carcasses was low, and finding them soon enough after death for their tissues to be suitable for most diagnostic tests was highly unlikely.

Allen and Shapton (1942:65-66) reported a simultaneous outbreak of an unknown viral disease among striped skunks and a widespread decline in skunk numbers in Michigan. Seven of 36 dens excavated contained skunks, four of which were dead, and several other dead skunks were scattered over their study area. Despite intensive field observations and livetrapping operations they were unable to account for 6 of 12 skunks marked in autumn and 3 of 8 marked in winter.

Five dead skunks which exhibited no evidence of injury were found in northwestern Illinois. Necropsies performed on these skunks revealed no gross pathological changes. Brain and salivary gland tissues from two of these skunks contained rabies viruses. Tissues from the remaining three skunks were not tested because of decomposition.

Pneumonia, distemper, rabies, and other diseases undoubtedly take a toll of skunks and, combined, may be one of the most important factors of mortality. Because of their density-dependent nature, one or more of several diseases may be important in maintaining the cyclic nature of population levels of striped skunks, as indicated by data presented by Lantz (1923:16) pertaining to sales of fur.

Starvation

While death due to starvation was even more difficult to detect among striped skunks than death resulting from diseases, it probably was at least an equally important cause of mortality among them. Each adult female striped skunk killed while lactating represented the loss of about six young skunks from starvation. In addition, some mortality must have resulted from starvation during winter. Striped skunks in northwestern Illinois frequently were forced to fast for periods as long as 3 months during winter. In this season, skunks lost an average of about half their prefasting body weights, possibly near the maximum if recovery was to occur. Individuals forced to retire to their winter dens earlier than usual, or individuals forced to remain in their dens during exceptionally prolonged winters, may not have accumulated sufficient fat to sustain them.

Table 23. *The estimated harvest of striped skunks in Illinois, based on annual reports by trappers to the Illinois Department of Conservation, each trapping season for which data were available, 1929–61.*

TRAPPING SEASON	NUMBER OF TRAPPING LICENSES SOLD	PERCENT OF TRAPPERS REPORTING	PERCENT OF TRAPPERS TAKING SKUNKS	AVERAGE NUMBER OF SKUNKS TAKEN PER SUCCESSFUL TRAPPER	ESTIMATED NUMBER OF SKUNKS CAUGHT IN ILLINOIS
1929–30	13,911	15	55	5.0	38,255
1930–31	11,575	10	59	5.9	40,291
1934–35	6,654	13	56	5.9	21,983
1935–36	6,480	14	45	4.7	13,705
1936–37	9,815	11	64	5.3	33,289
1937–38	12,560	23	49	3.7	22,770
1938–39	12,810	18	48	3.7	22,751
1939–40	16,615	11	48	3.7	29,951
1943–44	22,122	16.4	46.9	3.9	40,463
1944–45	22,636	9.5	43.6	1.9	18,751
1945–46	24,955	9.9	37.3	3.0	27,924
1946–47	30,949	8.4	34.1	2.6	27,440
1947–48	27,015	6.9	23.2	2.2	13,787
1948–49	26,788	6.2	27.3	2.2	16,089
1949–50	21,206	4.4	19.9	2.2	9,284
1950–51	18,262	5.5	13.8	2.0	5,040
1951–52	17,180	29.6	12.0	2.1	4,330
1954–55	8,445	4.8	13.9	1.0	1,174
1955–56	7,307	4.7	14.7	2.2	2,363
1956–57	7,302	4.5	8.6	2.4	1,507
1957–58	6,195	4.1	4.4	2.2	601
1958–59	5,234	4.0	2.9	1.2	182
1959–60	5,294	4.9	9.5	1.8	905
1960–61	6,607	2.8	8.0	1.4	741
1961–62	6,138	2.5	10.6	1.8	1,172

Accidents

Numerous carcasses of skunks along highways gave abundant evidence of mortality resulting from accidents. Although accidents were among the most obvious causes of death, it was difficult to evaluate their effect on population levels of striped skunks because of the many factors which influence numbers of skunks killed by automobiles: weather conditions, speed of automobiles, number of automobiles, quality of highways or roads, time of year, time of day, proximity of good skunk habitats to highways, and population levels of skunks.

Many skunks appeared to be killed by farm machines, especially by mowers. Eight of 14 striped skunks known to have died on the Shannon Study Area from causes other than trapping and handling were victims of farm machines; all were juveniles less than 4 months old and all were killed by mowers. Sickle bars on combines were usually set too high above the ground to kill skunks, but many skunks apparently lost the distal portions of their tails in encounters with these machines.

Harvest for Fur

Seton (1926:317) estimated that the harvest of striped skunks for fur in the United States between 1900 and 1915 averaged slightly more than 1.2 millions annually. Lantz (1923:16) presented data showing that an average of more than 615,000 skunk pelts (including *Spilogale*) were sold annually on the St. Louis, Missouri, market between 1918 and 1921. Mohr (1943:518) estimated that the catch of striped skunks in Illinois was about 80,000 in the 1929–30 trapping season and more than 36,000 in the 1939–40 season.

The estimated harvest of striped skunks in Illinois, based on annual reports by trappers to the Department of Conservation, each trapping season for which data were available between 1929 and 1961 are shown in Table 23. Although crude, these data indicate that mortality among striped skunks, resulting from harvest for fur, is insignificant at the present time.

Chapter XI

PARASITES AND DISEASES

ECTOPARASITES OF STRIPED SKUNKS IN NORTHWESTERN ILLINOIS

Two hundred forty striped skunks were examined for ectoparasites between July 1959 and August 1962. Freshly killed or anesthetized specimens were brushed and combed thoroughly for fleas and ticks, and complete collections of these forms were made. Samples of lice and of mites were collected from 28 skunks, and ears of 21 skunks were swabbed with cotton applicators in attempts to ascertain the presence of ear mites. Estimations of the relative infestation of striped skunks by lice were made for all specimens.

Ectoparasites were identified by Dr. Lewis J. Stannard, Jr., Section of Faunistic Surveys and Insect Identification, Illinois Natural History Survey.

Fleas

Twenty-nine (12.1 percent) of the 240 striped skunks examined were infested with a total of 68 fleas. Numbers of striped skunks examined and found to be infested with fleas, each month, and the number of each species of flea collected each month, are shown in Table 24.

Apparently, striped skunks have no flea fauna of their own but are accidentally infested with fleas associated primarily with other species of mammals (Table 25). Infestation of striped skunks by all species of fleas named, except one (*Orchopeas howardii*), can be explained on the basis of the relationship between striped skunks and the primary host species of the fleas.

Table 24. Numbers of striped skunks examined and found to be infested with fleas, and the number of each species of flea collected, each month, northwestern Illinois, July 1959–August 1962.

Month	Number of Skunks Examined	Number of Skunks Infested	Opisocrostis bruneri	Chaetopsylla lotoris	Oropsylla arctomys	Orchopeas howardii	Megabothris asio	Ctenophthalmus pseudagyrtes	Totals
			Species and Numbers of Fleas						
January	2	2		9	2				11
February	11	4		11	13				24
March	12	1		1	5				6
April	22	2				2			2
May	27	3	1		2				3
June	14	3	1			2			3
July	33	4	5						5
August	67	7	6		1		1	1	9
September	29	2	3						3
October	21	0							0
November	1	0							0
December	1	1			2				2
Totals	240	29	16	23	23	4	1	1	68

Striped skunks occupying dens in woodlands during winter were infested with *Oropsylla arctomys* and *Chaetopsylla lotoris*, species primarily associated with woodchucks and raccoons, respectively. Undoubtedly, woodchucks or raccoons, or both, were occupying or had been former occupants of dens from which these striped skunks were caught.

Opisocrostis bruneri was frequently collected from striped skunks in late spring and summer, seasons during which the primary host species (ground squirrels) were active. On the Shannon Study Area, observations of the construction of dens indicated that striped skunks modified ground squirrel dens which had been partially excavated by badgers. A few ground squirrel remains were found in the stomach contents of several skunks. Infestation of striped skunks by *O. bruneri* probably can be accounted for on the basis of these associations with ground squirrels.

Megabothris asio and *Ctenophthalmus pseudagyrtes* were frequently found on several species of small mammals in northwestern Illinois

Table 25. Species of fleas with which striped skunks in northwestern Illinois were infested, and the genera of mammals in northwestern Illinois reported to be primary hosts of each species of flea.

SPECIES OF FLEAS	GENERA OF PRIMARY HOSTS	AUTHORITY
Opisocrostis brunei	*Citellus*	Jellison (1947)
Chaetopsylla lotoris	*Procyon*	Fox (1940)
	Urocyon	Layne (1958)
Oropsylla arctomys	*Marmota*	Benton & Cerwonka (1960)
Orchopeas howardii	*Sciurus & Glaucomys*	Benton & Cerwonka (1960)
Megabothris asio	*Microtus*	Benton & Cerwonka (1960)
Ctenophthalmus pseudagyrtes	*Microtus, Peromyscus, Blarina, & Sorex*	Verts (1961b)
	Peromyscus, Microtus, Pitymys, Synaptomys, & Scalopus	Layne (1958)

(Verts 1961b:472). Occurrence of these hosts in the diets of skunks may explain the occasional infestation of skunks by these species of fleas.

Orchopeas howardii is usually associated with tree squirrels and flying squirrels. Occurrence of this species on four striped skunks cannot be explained on the basis of association of skunks with squirrels or their dens.

Absence of some species of fleas was nearly as difficult to explain as the presence of other species. *Orchopeas leucopus, Epitedia wenmanni, Monopsyllus wagneri,* and *Corrodopsylla curvata* were found on small mammals in northwestern Illinois (Verts 1961b:472). In late winter and spring, small mammals frequently occurred in the diet of striped skunks. None of these species of fleas, except perhaps *C. curvata,* showed a high degree of host specificity (Benton and Cerwonka 1960: 388-389, Verts 1961b:472). Apparently, these fleas find skunks to be unsuitable hosts and soon drop off; none was found in the stomach contents of the skunks.

The common rabbit flea, *Cediopsylla simplex,* abundant on cottontail rabbits in some areas in northwestern Illinois (Stannard and Pietsch 1958:10-11), also was absent from the flea fauna collected from skunks. The occasional occurrence of rabbit remains in the stomach contents of skunks may have been primarily carrion; fleas probably dropped off dead rabbits before the carcasses were found by skunks.

Lice

A single species of louse, *Trichodectes mephitidis,* was found on 121

Table 26. *Numbers of striped skunks examined and found to be infested with Trichodectes mephitidis, and estimated numbers of lice on infested skunks, each month, northwestern Illinois, 1959–62.*

Month	Number of Skunks Examined	Numbers of Lice on Skunks				Total Number of Skunks Infested
		None	Few*	Many†	Very Many‡	
January	2	–	–	2	–	2
February	11	8	1	2	–	3
March	12	8	4	–	–	4
April	22	7	14	1	–	15
May	27	15	11	1	–	12
June	14	9	4	1	–	5
July	33	19	12	2	–	14
August	67	23	30	10	4	44
September	29	13	6	6	4	16
October	21	16	5	–	–	5
November	1	–	1	–	–	1
December	1	1	–	–	–	0
Totals	240	119	88	25	8	121

* Estimated 1–100.
† Estimated 100–1,000.
‡ Estimated more than 1,000.

(50.4 percent) of the 240 striped skunks examined for ectoparasites. This was also the only species of louse collected from 74 striped skunks examined by Stegeman (1939:494) in New York. This louse has been reported from *Mephitis, Mustela* (=*Putorius*), *Bassaricus,* and *Spilogale* (Kellogg and Ferris 1915:70); of these hosts, only *Mephitis* and *Mustela* occur in northwestern Illinois.

Numbers of infested skunks and estimated numbers of lice per skunk appeared to be greatest in April, August, and September (Table 26). The highest numbers of skunks infested and the highest populations of lice were noted in August. Metcalf and Flint (1951:904-905) stated that the horse louse, *Bovicola equi* (=*Trichodectes equi*), breeds throughout the year but is more abundant in late winter or early spring than in summer. Apparently, little is known concerning the life history of *T. mephitidis,* but it is seemingly dissimilar from that of the horse louse.

Mites

Nine *Hirstionyssus staffordi* (Mesostigmata:Dermanyssidae), a single deutonymph of an unknown species (Mesostigmata:Laelaptidae), and a single female of another unknown species (Oribatei:Oribatulidae) were the only mites collected. No mites were found in the ears of the 21 skunks examined by swabbing with cotton applicators.

Ticks

Twenty-three (9.6 percent) of the 240 striped skunks examined were infested with ticks. The woodchuck tick, *Ixodes cookei*, and the variable wood tick, *Dermacentor variabilis*, were the only species collected. Numbers of skunks infested, and numbers of each species of ticks collected each month, are shown in Table 27. Numbers of ticks collected and numbers of infested skunks were greatest in May and June. No ticks were collected between November and March, or in September.

Bot Fly Larvae

Larvae of bot flies believed to be *Cuterebra* sp. were found in open ruptures, about 5 mm in diameter, in the skin on two striped skunks. The opening in the skin was in the shoulder region of one skunk and in the hip region of the other. Both these skunks were members of a litter of seven about 18 days old at the time the bots were found.

On May 23, 1962, this litter of seven was captured with the adult female by excavating a den. No evidence of infestation by bots was noted on that date. During the night of May 23-24, the adult female moved the young to another den about 250 yards away. On June 4, the young were examined again, and two were found to be infested by bots. On the night of June 12-13, the adult female moved five young to a third den. On June 13, the den used between May 24 and June 12 was excavated and no evidence of the two missing young was found. On June 28, five young were seen at the entrance of the third den.

Scott and Snead (1942:95) believed that warble-fly infestations may have contributed to the mortality of white-footed mice, possibly by reducing their efficiency in escaping predators. The presence or absence of bots probably would not affect the rate of predation on skunks 18 to 26 days old. Rainey (1956:590-591) could find no other cause of death of a wood rat infested by a large warble on its throat. It is possible that the disappearance of the two young skunks was directly related to their infestation by bots.

The infestation, by bots, of the two 18-day-old skunks may have occurred in one of the following ways:

1. The young became infested while they were being moved from one den to another on the night of May 23-24.

Table 27. Numbers of striped skunks examined and found to be infested with ticks, and numbers of each species of tick collected, each month, northwestern Illinois, 1959–62.

| MONTH | NUMBER OF SKUNKS EXAMINED | NUMBER OF SKUNKS INFESTED | NUMBERS OF TICKS | | |
			Ixodes cookei	Dermacentor variabilis	TOTALS
January	2	0	–	–	0
February	11	0	–	–	0
March	12	0	–	–	0
April	22	1	–	1	1
May	27	7	18	12	30
June	14	6	1	21	22
July	33	3	1	2	3
August	67	4	4	1	5
September	29	0	–	–	0
October	21	2	8	–	8
November	1	0	–	–	0
December	1	0	–	–	0
Totals	240	23	32	37	69

2. Eggs or first instar larvae were transported to the young on the fur of the adult female.

3. The adult bot flies entered the ground den and laid their eggs directly on the young skunks.

Beamer *et al.* (1943:49) found that eggs of *Cuterebra beameri*, a bot which infests wood rats, were laid around the entrances to wood rat houses. Allison (1953:38) believed that bots infesting gray squirrels in North Carolina laid their eggs on vegetation, and that the first instar larvae attached themselves to vegetation and awaited a suitable host.

Although the vegetation along the route used by the adult female skunk to move her young from one den to the other was very sparse (corn about 5 inches tall) and the young were exposed only a short time, it was believed that this period afforded the greatest opportunity for infestation by bots.

Trends in Rates of Infestation

Stegeman (1939:494) believed that external parasites of striped skunks "increase materially in numbers during the winter when the skunk remains within the den. Since fleas, mites and lice all complete their life cycle on the animal and in the nest, this is a natural consequence." Because all fleas found on striped skunks in northwestern Illinois were not obligatory parasites of skunks, the relationship between the primary host species and striped skunks probably was more important in determining the rates of infestation by these forms than the seasonal activity of striped skunks. The only species of ectoparasites more numerous in winter than in other seasons were the raccoon flea and the woodchuck flea. Even the obligatory parasite *Trichodectes mephitidis* was more abundant in summer than in winter. Thus, it appears that factors other than remaining within the den for extended periods influenced the rate of infestation of striped skunks by ectoparasites.

ENDOPARASITES

Species of helminth parasites of striped skunks, that had been reported up to about 1930, were listed by Stiles and Baker (1935:1176-77). Erickson (1946:496, 502) extended this list, up to about 1946. Because extensive surveys of the helminth parasites of striped skunks have been made since 1946, because new species of parasites from striped skunks have been described, and because there appears to be some confusion concerning the species of skunks involved in some of the older surveys, a list of all helminth parasites reported from *Mephitis mephitis* (or its synonyms), and the authority for reporting the parasites from this species, are presented (Table 28).

Rates of infestation of striped skunks by some of the common helminth parasites of the species (*Alaria taxideae, Mesocestoides latus, M. variabilis, Ascaris columnaris,* and *Physaloptera maxillaris*) as reported by Babero (1960:26-27), Erickson (1946:499-500), Self and McKnight (1950:59-60), Hamilton (1936:240), Stegeman (1939:495), and Mead (1963:166-167) exhibited no clear-cut geographical trends. The wide variety of animal foods eaten by striped skunks, and the wide distribution of probable or known intermediate hosts of these parasites (slugs, frogs, grasshoppers, voles, and others) may be prime causes of the apparent lack of geographical relationships.

Intestinal Endoparasites of Striped Skunks in Northwestern Illinois

Intestinal tracts of 153 striped skunks collected between 1960 and 1962 in northwestern Illinois were examined for helminth parasites. Eighty-four (54.9 percent) were infested with one or more species of helminths; 10 were infested with cestodes, 50 with nematodes, and 24 with both nematodes and cestodes. Three skunks were infested with acanthocephalans, but none was infested with trematodes. Samples of

Table 28. Helminth and pentastomid parasites reported from striped skunks, and the authority reporting each species from this host, 1927–65.

SPECIES	AUTHORITY
TREMATODA	
Alaria taxideae	Swanson and Erickson (1946)
Alaria canadensis	Webster and Wolfgang (1956)
Brachylaime virginianum	Babero (1960)
Sellacotyle mustelae	Wallace (1935) (experimental)
Euryhelmis pyriformis	Webster and Wolfgang (1956)
Apophallus venustus	Webster and Wolfgang (1956)
Psilostomum sp.	Babero (1960)
CESTODA	
Mesocestoides variabilis	Mueller (1927)
Mesocestoides latus	Mueller (1927)
Mesocestoides corti	Mead (1963)
Oochoristica oklahomensis	Babero (1960)
Oochoristica pedunculata	Chandler (1952)
Oochoristica mephitis	Skinker (1935)
Anoplocephala sp.	Stegeman (1939)
Taenia sp.	Stiles and Baker (1935)
NEMATODA	
Ascaris columnaris	Stiles and Baker (1935)
Ascaris dasypodina	Stiles and Baker (1935)
Crenosoma mephitidis	Hobmaier (1941)
Crenosoma microbursa	Wallace (1941)
Molineus barbatus	Babero (1960)
Molineus patens	Babero (1960)
Physaloptera turgida	Leigh (1940)
Physaloptera maxillaris	Stiles and Baker (1935)
Dracunculus insiginis	Erickson (1946)
Filaria martis	Tiner (1946)
Filaroides milksi	Levine *et al.* (1965)
Skrjabingylus chitwoodorum	Hill (1939)
Strongyloides papillosus	Stiles and Baker (1935)
Arthrocephalis lotoris	Dikmans and Goldberg (1949)
Dipetalonema sp.	Babero (1960)
Gnathostoma sp.	Babero (1960)
Trichinella spiralis	Spindler and Permenter (1951)
Trichinella sp.	Babero (1960)
Gongylonema pulchrum	Goldberg (1954)
ACANTHOCEPHALA	
Macracanthorhynchus ingens	Van Cleave (1953)
Pachysentis canicola	Van Cleave (1953)
Moniliformis clarki	Van Cleave (1953)
Acanthocephala sp.	Tiner (1946)
PENTASTOMIDA	
Porocephalus subcylindricum	Stiles and Baker (1935)

helminths collected from 29 striped skunks collected throughout the year in northwestern Illinois included the following species:

Mesocestoides variabilis
Oochoristica mephitis
Ascaris columnaris
Molineus patens
Physaloptera maxillaris
Arthrocephalis lotoris
Macracanthorhynchus ingens

There were no significant differences between rates of infestation among different sex- and age-classes of striped skunks, but no skunk younger than about 3 months old was examined. Young skunks would not become infested with intestinal parasites acquired by ingestion of intermediate hosts until they had fed on these intermediate hosts for some time.

Stegeman (1939:494) reported that among 74 striped skunks collected in New York, those taken in late summer and autumn were more heavily infested with intestinal parasites than those examined in late winter and spring. He attributed the seasonal difference in rates of infestation to starvation of the parasites when the digestive tracts of the skunks were empty during their period of dormancy in winter. In northwestern Illinois, in addition to the seasonal cycle described by Stegeman, rates of infestation appeared to decline in midsummer and to increase rapidly in early autumn (Fig. 46). It appeared highly unlikely that the midsummer decline in the rate of infestation could be attributed to starvation of the host species. Numbers of intermediate hosts of many species of helminths available to striped skunks appeared to be greater during summer than at other seasons. No explanation for the decline in numbers of skunks infested with intestinal helminths during midsummer can be presented on the bases of known habits or behavior of hosts or parasites.

Nonintestinal Helminth Endoparasites of Striped Skunks

Grinnell *et al.* (1937:353) reported nematodes under the skin on the hind legs, back, and shoulders of striped skunks in California; Erickson (1946:496) postulated that these parasites were a "filarid species." Cheatum and Cook (1948:421) and Erickson (1946:500) reported the guinea worm, *Dracunculus insignis,* from beneath the skin of striped skunks in New York and Minnesota, respectively. Spindler and Permenter (1951:19) found *Trichinella spiralis* in muscle tissue of striped skunks. Hobmaier (1941:229) reported a nematode, *Creno-soma mephitidis*, from the bronchi of skunks, and Goble (1942*a*:381) reported *C. zederi* from the same site. These two species of *Creno-soma* are now considered to be synonymous (Erickson 1946:496). *Crenosoma microbursa* also were reported from the bronchi of striped

Fig. 46. Monthly rates of infestation of striped skunks by intestinal helminth parasites, northwestern Illinois, 1960–62. Numerals indicate numbers of skunks examined each month.

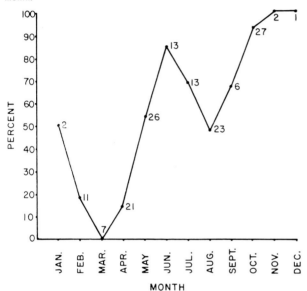

skunks (Wallace 1941:58). Lungs and flesh beneath the skin of skunks caught in northwestern Illinois were not examined for parasites.

Hill (1939:475) described a nematode, *Skrjabingylus chitwoodorum*, from frontal sinuses of striped skunks, and Levine *et al.* (1962:3) reported finding this species within the brain case of skunks. Infestations by this nematode are frequently characterized by swelling or erosion (or both) of the frontal bones of striped skunks (Fig. 47), but Levine *et al.* (1962:5) reported that no such lesions were observed among skunks which had *S. chitwoodorum* in their brain cases. Goble (1942*b*:96-97) found *S. chitwoodorum* in 18 of 25 skunks examined from New York, and Stegeman (1939:495) reported that swellings and erosion of the frontal bones occurred in 26 of more than 150 skulls collected in New York. Of 164 striped skunks caught in northwestern Illinois, 108 (65.9

percent) of the skulls had lesions characteristic of those made by infestations by *S. chitwoodorum.*

Fig. 47. Dorsal and lateral views of skulls of striped skunks, showing relative amounts of swelling and erosion caused by infestation by *Skrjabingylus chitwoodorum.* Left, no damage; center, moderate damage; right, severe damage.

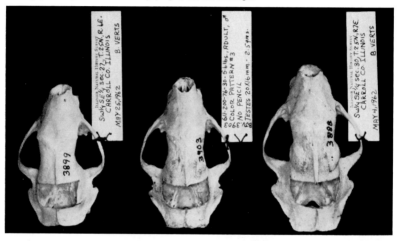

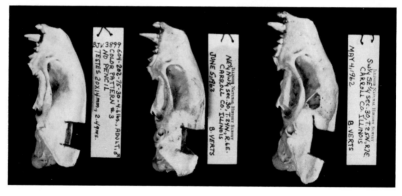

DISEASES

Many species of wildlife are known or suspected reservoirs of zoonoses. However, diseases unknown or rarely occurring in man or his domestic animals may have equal or greater impact on population levels of some species of wildlife than zoonotic diseases. For instance, Allen and Shapton (1942:65-66) reported that nearly half the estimated population of striped skunks on their study area in Michigan died of what they believed was an unknown virus disease. Diseases of wildlife species not considered to be zoonoses, or diseases of little importance to veterinary public health, frequently are ignored unless an important game species becomes infected.

The importance of the role of striped skunks in the epizootiology of certain zoonoses, especially rabies and leptospirosis, has been recognized relatively recently. Because of the importance of these zoonoses, and because population levels of striped skunks appear to fluctuate widely from unknown causes, it seems appropriate to discuss all diseases with which striped skunks are known to become infected.

Because the principal objective of this investigation was to define the role of striped skunks in the epizootiology of rabies, this disease will be discussed in a separate chapter.

Leptospirosis

A marked increase in the prevalence of leptospirosis in man, domestic animals, and wildlife occurred in the United States between 1950 and 1960 (Steele 1960:247). The threat to public health and losses to the livestock industry caused by leptospirosis were undoubtedly among the factors which prompted investigation of several species of wildlife as possible reservoirs of the disease. Striped skunks were frequently included among species on which investigations were conducted.

McKeever *et al.* (1958a:648) were apparently first to isolate *Leptospira* from striped skunks, with the identification of *L. pomona* and *L. ballum* from specimens taken in Georgia. Galton *et al.* (1960:919) isolated a new subserotype from skunks, which they designated *L. mini georgia*. *L. canicola* (Roth *et al.* 1961:335) and *L. australis* (Roth 1961:18) were isolated from striped skunks collected in Louisiana. Gorman *et al.* (1962:519) reported the isolation of *L. hebdomadis, L. hyos,* and *L. grippotyphosa* from striped skunks caught in Georgia. Roth *et al.* (1963a:18) added *L. hyos hyos, L. icterohaemorrhagiae,* and a strain of the *australis* serogroup to the list of serotypes isolated from striped skunks. Thus, within a period of less than 5 years, 11 serotypes and subserotypes of *Leptospira* were isolated from striped skunks in the United States.

McKeever *et al.* (1958a:649) reported that 13.6 percent of 132 striped skunks collected in southwestern Georgia were infected with leptospires. McKiel *et al.* (1961:17) reported isolates from two of ten skunks caught in eastern Canada. Roth (1961:18) reported isolating *Leptospira* from 60.1 percent of 286 striped skunks in Louisiana, and

Roth *et al.* (1963*a*:17) isolated leptospires from 57.4 percent of 650 striped skunks in Louisiana. Gorman *et al.* (1962:520) found 15.8 percent of 430 striped skunks in Georgia to be infected with leptospires. Clark (1962:145) reported a 33.3 percent rate of infection among striped skunks in Pennsylvania. Roth *et al.* (1963*a*:18) found that 3.5 percent of 650 striped skunks supported multiple infections of *Leptospira* serotypes. Although the incidence of leptospirosis among striped skunks indicated by bacteriologic studies varied from place to place, it was often higher among striped skunks than among other species of wildlife in the same area.

Interpretation of serologic studies of leptospirosis is somewhat difficult because of (1) frequent cross-reactions between serotypes, (2) a period early in the infection during which antibodies have not yet been formed, (3) a decline in titer level with time, and (4) differences caused by different methods of testing sera. Roth *et al.* (1963*a*:21) found that the overall incidence of leptospirosis among 277 striped skunks as revealed by serologic tests was not grossly different from that revealed by bacteriologic tests, but in the cases of several serotypes, bacteriologic incidence exceeded serologic incidence, and among other serotypes the reverse was true. Despite obvious disadvantages of depending entirely on serologic tests to reveal characteristics of the disease among a wild population, such tests are much easier and less time-consuming than bacteriologic tests.

Serum samples from 106 striped skunks collected in northwestern Illinois between 1958 and 1962 were tested by microscopic agglutination (agglutination-lysis) by Dr. D. H. Ferris, College of Veterinary Medicine, University of Illinois. Tenfold dilutions of 1:10 to 1:100,000 of the following live antigens were used: *Leptospira ballum, L. grippotyphosa, L. pomona, L. icterohaemorrhagiae, L. canicola, L. sejroe,* and *L. hyos.* Sera from 37 (34.9 percent) of the 106 skunks reacted with one or more antigens at a dilution of 1:100 or greater; 12 reacted with *L. pomona*, 3 with *L. grippotyphosa*, and 26 with *L. ballum.* Four *L. ballum–L. pomona* cross-reactions occurred.

Sex ratios of infected and noninfected striped skunks collected by Roth *et al.* (1963*a*:21) were not significantly different. Sex ratios of reactors and nonreactors collected in northwestern Illinois were also not significantly different ($X^2 = 0.004$, df = 1). Reactor rates (all serotypes combined) among adults were significantly greater than among juveniles ($P < 0.02$); when only reactors to *L. ballum* were considered, there was a significant difference at the 0.1 level but not at the 0.05 level ($X^2 = 3.33$, df = 1). The greater frequency of reactors among adults may indicate (1) relatively few juveniles became infected between the time they were born and the time they entered their wintering dens, or (2) there was not a rapid decline in titer as has been observed among some other species (Ferris *et al.* 1960:241), or (3) perhaps both.

Roth *et al.* (1963*a*:34-36) attempted to define the role of striped skunks in the epizootiology of leptospirosis caused by several serotypes of *Leptospira.* They believed that striped skunks were possible primary hosts of *L. hyos hyos,* accidental hosts of *L. grippotyphosa* and *L. icterohaemorrhagiae,* and possible secondary hosts of *L. ballum* and *L. canicola.* They were unsure of the status of skunks in the case of *L. mini georgia* because of the relatively few isolations and reactors in their sample. They believed that striped skunks played a significant role in the epizootiology of leptospirosis caused by *L. pomona,* but were hesitant to call skunks primary reservoirs of the serotype because of the role of livestock in maintaining the disease. Roth (1961:18) believed that striped skunks were accidental hosts of *L. australis.*

In a subsequent study, Roth *et al.* (1963*b*:994-1000) reported that the duration of leptospiruria in naturally infected striped skunks in Louisiana was as long as 321 days for those infected with *L. pomona,* 774 days for those infected with *L. hyos hyos,* 400 days for those infected with *L. canicola,* 167 days for those infected with *L. icterohaemorrhagiae,* and 47 days for those infected with *L. ballum.* They believed that these observations tended to corroborate their previous conclusions that striped skunks were the primary reservoir of *L. hyos hyos,* played an important role in the epizootiology of *L. canicola* (although dogs played the major role), and could perpetuate infections of *L. pomona* in the absence of cattle and swine.

Leptospira pomona infections have been shown to be prevalent among livestock in northwestern Illinois (Ferris and Verts 1964:37). Differences in reactor rates of livestock and striped skunks tended to indicate that skunks were accidental hosts of *L. pomona* in northwestern Illinois. Reactor rates among cattle and swine in Illinois to *L. pomona* were much greater than reactor rates to *L. grippotyphosa* (Hanson and Pickard 1958:41-42), but among white-tailed deer the reactor rates were approximately equal (Ferris *et al.* 1961*a*:893, Ferris and Verts 1964:37-38). These data, plus the fact that *L. grippotyphosa* has not been isolated from wild animals and only once from domestic animals in Illinois (Hanson *et al.* 1964:495-496), make interpretation of the significance of a very few reactors to *L. grippotyphosa* even more difficult. Absence of isolations, and relatively low reactor rates, probably indicate that skunks are accidental hosts of *L. grippo-typhosa*. House mice, a common food item of skunks, are considered to be the primary reservoir species of *L. ballum* (Roth *et al.* 1963*a*:35). The predator-prey relationship between the two species is probably a factor influencing the reactor rate to *L. ballum* among striped skunks; the high reactor rate possibly indicates that skunks are secondary hosts.

Q Fever

Although serologic evidence of Q fever infections has been reported in man (Luoto 1960:139, Kitze *et al.* 1957:245, Shepard 1947:185) and in livestock (Luoto 1960:137, Ferris *et al.* 1961*b*:1113) in several midwestern states, the potential of wildlife species as reservoirs of *Coxiella burneti* apparently has received little attention. Among livestock in Illinois, the highest reactor rate occurred in the northern part of the state (Ferris *et al.* 1961*b*:1113).

To survey the prevalence of Q fever among striped skunks in northwestern Illinois, 52 serum samples were tested by the capillary-agglutination test (Luoto 1953) by Dr. D. H. Ferris, College of Veterinary Medicine, University of Illinois. Only two (3.9 percent) sera reacted. Because reactor rates among livestock in northwestern Illinois as high as 50 percent have been reported (Ferris *et al.* 1961*b*: 1112), the relatively low percent of reactors among skunks was believed to indicate that skunks were not important reservoirs of the disease.

Listeriosis

Listeria monocytogenes was isolated from wild striped skunks in North Dakota (Bolin *et al.* 1955:49) and California (Osebold *et al.* 1957: 473). Gray (1964:211), in a review of listeriosis in wildlife, stated: "The material presented suggests that many different feral hosts may harbor *L. monocytogenes*, but it does not support the notion that *listeric infection* is widespread among them."

Because of a similarity of symptoms of listeriosis and rabies, *L. mono-cytogenes* might be isolated more frequently than it has been in the past by culturing material from skunks exhibiting symptoms of rabies but whose neurons do not contain Negri bodies.

Pulmonary Aspergillosis

Aspergillus fumigatus was isolated from a very young captive striped skunk in Missouri (Durant and Doll 1939:646). The suspected source of infection was mouldy grain in the basement where the skunk was kept.

The prevalence of this disease among wild skunks is unknown, but in years when exceptionally high rainfall occurs it is possible that damp, mouldy nesting material in dens with poor drainage could be a source of infection of this disease in skunks.

Pleuritis

A pleuritis condition was reported in a wild skunk in Ohio, but organisms involved in the infection were not reported (Junod and Bezdek 1945:309).

Ringworm

Menges and Georg (1957:505) examined two striped skunks for ringworm, but none was infected. McKeever *et al.* (1958*b*:974) examined 239 striped skunks and found no *Trichophyton mentagrophytes*. They isolated an apparently nonpathogenic Microsporum (red variety) from two skunks.

Murine Typhus

Morlan *et al.* (1950:60-61) tested sera from 109 striped skunks for murine typhus antibodies by compliment-fixation. Serum from one skunk had a positive titer at a dilution of 1:8. Brigham (1938:2079) inoculated a striped skunk with typhus; although the skunk exhibited no signs of illness, the virus was recovered 16 days after inoculation.

Chagas' Disease

Brooke *et al.* (1957:15) found haemoflagellates with *Trypanosoma cruzi*–like characters in the blood of a skunk caught in southern Georgia. Norman *et al.* (1959:457) found 1.1 percent of 306 striped skunks caught in southern Georgia and northern Florida to be infected with *T. cruzi*–like haemoflagellates. They stated that triatomid bugs were rare and that no human cases of Chagas' disease had been reported in the area from which infected skunks were obtained.

Tularemia

McKeever *et al.* (1958*c*:122) found antibodies to *Pasteurella tularensis* in 21.5 percent of 311 striped skunks collected in southern Georgia.

Sixty-five sera had titers which they considered significant (dilutions of 1:80 or more). They believed that striped skunks were one of the chief mammalian reservoirs of tularemia.

Histoplasmosis

Emmons *et al.* (1955:41) isolated *Histoplasma capsulatum* from 2 of 18 striped skunks in Virginia. A striped skunk was reported to be infected in Kansas (Menges *et al.* 1955:66).

Acute Bronchopneumonia

Several wild striped skunks between 25 and 45 days old were caught or were brought to me by persons interested in my study of skunks. These skunks usually could be reared successfully if they were old enough to eat soft foods from dishes, or if a lactating captive female could be induced to adopt them. Attempts to feed milk to young skunks, with the aid of an eyedropper or doll bottle, invariably resulted in death of the animals. It was extremely difficult to use these devices to feed milk to skunks without occasionally permitting milk to enter their tracheae and lungs. A lung from one of the skunks that died was submitted for examination to the Diagnostic Laboratory of the College of Veterinary Medicine, University of Illinois. The following diagnostic report was received: "This lung specimen manifests an extensive acute bronchopneumonia, some interstitial pneumonitis with compensatory emphysema and considerable congestion." An irritation of the lungs from inhalation of milk apparently caused the bronchopneumonia.

Brucellosis

Sera from 52 striped skunks caught in northwestern Illinois were tested by the serum agglutination plate test for antibodies to *Brucella abortus* by Dr. D. H. Ferris, College of Veterinary Medicine, University of Illinois. None of the sera reacted.

Canine Distemper

Helmboldt and Jungherr (1955:464) diagnosed canine distemper in a striped skunk which exhibited symptoms of rabies but had no Negri bodies in its neurons and was negative by mouse inoculation for rabies. They diagnosed canine distemper in a group of animals of several species, either by ferret inoculation or by presence of pathognomonic inclusion bodies. Goss (1948:66) reported that skunks (species not recorded) were susceptible to viruses of Carré, the etiologic agent of canine distemper.

Miscellaneous Diseases

Fox (1923:252, 276, 312) recorded acute pancreatitis, nephritis, and an inflammatory condition of the mammary gland (mastitis?) in skunks in capitivity (species not recorded), and also reported (p. 156) an abscess of the lung in a striped skunk. Richards (1957:4) implied that skunks contracted erysipelas and lymphocytic choriomeningitis, in addition to several of the other diseases listed previously.

Chapter XII

RABIES

The study of zoonoses, such as rabies, in wild mammals may be approached from either of two viewpoints: that of characteristics of the disease or that of characteristics of the species infected. A complete understanding of the disease-host relationship requires both approaches, but certain characteristics of the disease (etiology, modes of transmission, rates of mortality, and others) must be at least partially understood before the latter approach is indicated.

Most previous investigations of rabies reflected characteristics of the disease, with emphasis on relative infectivity among various species, methods of transmission, diagnostic techniques, and preventative measures. Studies concerned with relative incidence, geographical distribution, seasonal incidence, and other aspects of the epizootiology of rabies were based on data collected by state public health agencies.

The objectives of the present study were to determine which characteristics of striped skunks and of their populations appeared to be related to prevalence of rabies among them. This approach appeared to have been neglected. Before discussing relationships between striped skunks and prevalence of rabies among them, it seems appropriate to review briefly current knowledge concerning the disease.

ETIOLOGY, TRANSMISSION, SYMPTOMS, PATHOLOGY, AND MORTALITY

Rabies is an encephalitic disease of endothermic animals (Johnson 1959:405) caused by the filterable virus *Formido inexorabilis* (Merchant and Packer 1961:793). Galloway and Elford (1936:534) believed the virus to be about 100 to 150 mμ in diameter, and Matsumoto (1962:199) obtained electron photomicrographs of double-walled elongated particles about 100 to 130 mμ in diameter which he believed to be rabies virus. However, Almeida *et al.* (1962:148-149) obtained electron photomicrographs of particles they thought to be rabies virus which were about 250 to 400 mμ in diameter, had surface projections about 100 Å long, and contained long twisted ribbons.

Johnson (1959:415-416) indicated that the infectivity of rabies virus is lost in 1 to 2 weeks when tissues containing them are exposed to the air at room temperature, but may be retained for a year or more when stored in glycerol at below-freezing temperatures. He further indicated that repeated freezing and thawing reduces the infectivity of the virus, and that sunlight, ultraviolet irradiation, bichloride of mercury, formalin, and strong acids and bases destroy the virus. Rabies virus is resistant to all known antibiotics.

Under natural conditions rabies is restricted to mammals, but the virus can be cultivated in tissue cultures and in chicken and duck embryos. Birds may be artificially infected, but other vertebrates are refractory (Kelser 1955:262). In North America, the disease is most commonly reported among members of the mammalian families Mustelidae, Canidae, Procyonidae, Vespertilionidae, and Molossidae. Johnson (1959:405) believed that the "permanent hosts" were among members of the family Mustelidae.

Rabies virus in saliva of infected individuals is transmitted to noninfected individuals by biting (Johnson 1959:405), but not all infected individuals are capable of transmitting the virus. Tierkel (1959:191) stated that 54 to 90 percent of animals dying of rabies have virus in their salivary glands. Recent evidence indicates that aerosol transmission may occur in certain cave environments (Constantine 1962:289). Circumstantial evidence indicates that the virus may possibly be transmitted in milk from one individual to another (Kelser 1955:277, Johnson 1960:273). Because of pathologic evidence of rabies virus in the kidneys of some individual animals (Johnson 1959:417), transmission in urine may be possible. Natural transmission of rabies by arthropod vectors has not been demonstrated; when artificially introduced into ticks, rabies virus persists a relatively short time (Bell *et al.* 1957:282). Soave (1966:44-46) demonstrated transmission of rabies by ingestion of infected tissue. While cognizant of other modes of transmission, most workers appear to believe that transmission of rabies by biting is the method of greatest epizootiological significance. Other methods require specific conditions too infrequently encountered to be significant or occur so rarely as to be considered medical curiosities.

The incubation period of rabies varies between 10 and 240 days (Johnson 1959:405), depending on the recipient species, donor species, location and extent of wounds, quantity of virus introduced, and virulence of the virus (Kelser 1955:262). By intracerebral serial passage of rabies virus in a given host species, the incubation period becomes progressively shorter until it reaches 6 or 7 days (Rhodes and van Rooyen 1962:400). Such modified virus is said to be fixed (*virus fixe*). This virus tends to cause paralytic symptoms, does not multiply in the salivary glands, and loses much of its virulence when introduced by peripheral routes (Johnson 1959:414). Rapid passage under natural conditions may cause similar attenuation of the virus, which may tend to reduce spread of the disease.

Although the rate of infectivity of rabies virus among wild mammals after exposure by natural modes of transmission is unknown, the probability that an individual contracts the disease after exposure may be relatively low. Rhodes and van Rooyen (1962:392) stated that among humans only about 15 percent of those bitten by rabid dogs contract the disease in absence of treatment. Variables which influence the incubation period, plus the degree of inherent immunity of exposed individuals, appear to be factors determining the rate of infectivity. Age of the exposed individual also appears to be an important factor; young animals are more susceptible than older ones (Tierkel 1959: 193). Because of these variables, it is extremely difficult to make a reliable estimate of the relative efficiency of the normal mode of transmission of the disease among wild mammals. It appears certain, however, that all individuals exposed to the disease do not contract it.

Rabies is usually considered to be neurotropic, but this is partly based on the absence of demonstrable viremia (Johnson 1959:411, 413). However, Sanderson (personal communication) isolated virus from spleens, pancreases, adrenal glands, and kidneys of experimentally infected raccoons; Barr (1961:54) isolated rabies virus from adrenal glands, kidneys, and spinal cord, but not from spleen, liver, and lungs of an experimentally infected opossum; and Sulkin *et al.* (1957:463) found virus in brown fat of experimentally inoculated free-tailed bats. Borodina (1959:100) recovered virus from blood of mice up to 54 hours after they were inoculated with rabies, and concluded that viremia occurred early in the incubation period but not during the symptomatic period.

Gross abnormalities specifically diagnostic of the disease are absent, but several degenerative changes of neurons have been demonstrated (Johnson 1959:410-412). Characteristic inclusion bodies (Negri bodies) in the neurons (most abundant in neurons of the hippocampus major) are considered diagnostic. Negri bodies, thought to be aggregations of virus (Rhodes and van Rooyen 1962:401), are absent in about 10 to 12 percent of the individuals diagnosed as rabid by the mouse inoculation technique (Merchant and Packer 1961:800).

Symptoms of rabies in animals are variable but usually fall within two broad categories: paralytic rabies (dumb rabies) in which the infected animal develops progressive paralysis, usually beginning in the hind limbs, and furious rabies in which the infected animal is agitated, vicious, and aggressive (Kelser 1955:263). Intermediate forms are sometimes recognized (Richards 1957:4). Differences in manifestations of the disease appear to be more closely related to species of host than to strains of virus. In fact, no distinct immunological strains of rabies virus have been identified (Tierkel 1959:189).

Currently, there is no specific treatment for the disease once symptoms develop, but there appears to be a growing belief that spontaneous recovery from the paralytic form of the disease can occur (Constantinesco and Birzu 1958:739, Thiery 1959:33, Johnson 1959:410). Recurrent rabies and asymptomatic carriers of the disease have been reported among vampire bats (Johnson 1959:424) and among terrestrial mammals (Thiery 1959:33). The absence of demonstrable rabies virus in saliva or nervous tissue of terrestrial species at times other than during a lethal infection is strong evidence of absolute lethality of the disease among this group of mammals. Merchant and Packer (1961:796) stated: "There are probably no recoveries in natural cases of rabies, although some experimentally inoculated animals may show an abortive type of illness and recover."

Extremely long incubation periods are occasionally observed among wild and among experimentally infected mammals. Among experimental animals there appears to be an inverse correlation between quantity of virus with which animals are inoculated and length of the incubation period (Sikes 1962:1043, Table 1). Among wild animals the incubation period may be related to the mode of transmission (Johnson 1960:273). The site (or sites) at which rabies virus is maintained during these long incubation periods in terrestrial species is apparently unknown, although proliferation of the virus can occur in several tissues and organs. There is some evidence that prolonged incubation periods may be the reactivation of latent rabies virus by some unrelated stimulus (Koprowski 1952:963). Among bats, rabies virus in brown fat does not proliferate when the animals are hibernating, but does so when the animals are aroused (Sulkin *et al.* 1960:613). Sulkin (1962:496-497) postulated that this was the "reservoiring mechanism" of rabies in bats. Among terrestrial mammals, cortisone was demonstrated to have a "pro-infective" action in rabbits inoculated with rabies virus (Patera 1956:667-669), and the same or similar drugs appeared to reactivate, at times, latent rabies virus in guinea pigs (Soave *et al.* 1961:1360) and in raccoons (Sanderson, personal communication). Some of the exceptionally long incubation periods observed among naturally infected wild mammals may represent natural reactivation of latent rabies virus. Koprowski (1952:964) cited a case of rabies in a human in which the virus was believed to have been reactivated by bacterial pneumonia.

Tierkel (1959:189) stated: "The introduction of rabies virus in an animal as a natural or artificial infection or as a vaccinal antigen stimulates the production of specific antibodies. . . ." Atanasiu *et al.* (1956: 603) found that serum-neutralizing (SN) antibodies were not elicited in humans by a single injection of Flury strain live-virus vaccine or by a single injection of phenol-killed virus vaccine as frequently as by multiple injections of phenol-killed vaccine. Sikes (1962:1046) found SN antibodies in serum of only 4 of 12 foxes and 1 of 12 skunks inoculated with rabies virus. Barr (1961:59-60) found that only 3 of 17 opossums inoculated with rabies developed SN antibodies, but that 10 of 14 without demonstrable SN antibodies successfully resisted infection. Thus, it appears that while the presence of SN antibodies indicates prior introduction of rabies virus, the introduction of rabies virus does not always elicit an antibody response. There is also some evidence that different species respond differently to experimental inoculation with rabies virus. The physiological and epizootiological significance of SN antibodies does not appear to be sufficiently clear to permit complete understanding of their presence or absence among populations of wild mammals during periods of enzootic or epizootic rabies.

In light of present knowledge, there appear to be four possible courses when an individual animal is naturally inoculated with rabies virus:

1. No symptoms develop, and virus cannot be demonstrated in any tissues.

2. Symptoms develop after a "normal" period of incubation, and death ensues several days thereafter. Transmission of virus may or may not be possible during and just prior to symptomatic stages.

3. The virus becomes latent, to become active after several months, possibly because of some unrelated stimulus.

4. No symptoms develop, but transmissible virus occurs in the saliva irregularly or continuously for several months.

HISTORY AND DISTRIBUTION OF RABIES IN THE UNITED STATES

Existence of rabies in North America before advent of white man is problematical. It appears reasonable to assume that rabies occurred, at least among those species of Canidae that have a circumpolar distribution, for a considerable period of time before discovery of the New World. Rabies was known to have occurred in Europe at least as early as the 13th century B.C. (Kelser 1955:250). Rhodes and van Rooyen (1962:395) believed that rabies has been present among arctic foxes "for generations."

Records of rabies in dogs in Virginia in 1753 and in North Carolina in 1762 (Johnson 1959:406) are among the earliest records of the disease in the United States. Gier (1948:143) recorded a report of an epizootic of rabies in foxes in Massachusetts in 1812. Outbreaks of rabies in foxes in other parts of eastern United States have continued to occur up to the present time (Gier 1948:143, Wood 1954:132-135, Parker *et al.* 1957:219, Jennings *et al.* 1960:171-172, Linhart 1960: 2-3). The earliest account of rabies in skunks appears to be a record of the disease in spotted skunks in Lower California in 1826 (Johnson 1960:270). Coues (1877:224-235) quoted authors who reported cases of rabies in man, resulting from bites of skunks, in Virginia, Michigan, Illinois, Kansas, Missouri, Colorado, and Texas. There was a widespread conviction at that time that the bite of a skunk invariably resulted in rabies infection. Gier (1948:143) cited records of rabies epizootics in skunks in Kansas in 1875 and in Arizona in 1907 and 1910. Parker (1962:273) stated that rabies in skunks nearly disappeared from the Midwest for several years after the outbreak of the disease in the Plains States in the 1870's. He cited, as evidence for his statement, the conclusion of Lantz (1923:18) that "The popular belief that hydrophobia will result from a skunk bite is in error." Seton (1926:345-347) pointed out that rabies in skunks was most commonly reported in southwestern United States and that relatively few individuals were infected.

From 1938 to 1962, there was a decline in the numbers of cases of rabies reported in the United States (Fig. 48). Much of this decline

probably can be attributed to better and more rigidly enforced legisla-
tion than had existed previously concerning control of the disease in
domestic carnivores. Reported cases of rabies in dogs and cats declined
from a peak of 9,486 in 1946 to 797 in 1962. Among wildlife species,
reported cases of rabies increased from 44 in 1938 to 2,314 in 1962
(Fig. 48). This reversal in comparative numbers of cases of rabies re-

Fig. 48. Numbers of cases of rabies reported in the United States in all species, in dogs
and cats, and in wildlife each year, 1938–62. Adapted from data from the Communicable
Disease Center (1961:8 and 1963a:3).

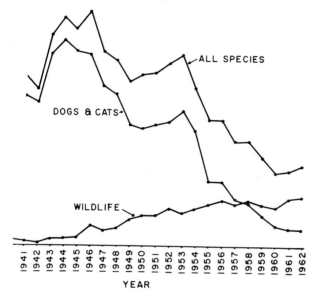

ported in domestic carnivores and in wildlife species changed rabies
from a disease primarily of dogs and cats to a disease primarily of
wildlife.

Although no area of the United States is probably completely free of
rabies, very few cases are reported in mountainous areas of northwestern United States and in New England (Fig. 49). Almost all
other states reported an average of 10 or more cases of rabies annually
between 1958 and 1962.

More than 90 percent of the 19,462 cases of rabies reported among
wild mammals between 1953 and 1962 occurred in either foxes or
skunks (Communicable Disease Center 1963a:3). Within this 10-year
period, skunks replaced foxes as the species of wildlife most frequently

reported to be infected (Fig. 50). Tierkel (1958:446, Fig. 2) believed
that areas from which rabies in skunks was reported were discrete from
areas from which rabies in foxes was reported. He later indicated some
overlap in skunk-rabies and fox-rabies areas (Tierkel 1959:196, Fig. 3).
In 1961 and 1962 combined, 23 of the 48 contiguous states reported
rabies in both foxes and skunks, but there was no correlation between
numbers of cases of rabies in skunks and numbers of cases of rabies in
foxes ($r = -0.002$). Population levels of foxes in skunk-rabies areas,
and of skunks in fox-rabies areas, did not appear to be appreciably

Fig. 49. Distribution of reported cases of rabies in all species in the United States,
based on the average number of cases reported in each state, 1958–62. Adapted from
data from the Communicable Disease Center (1963a:4).

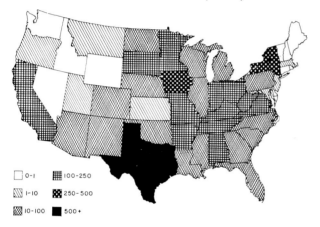

0-1   100-250

1-10   250-500

10-100   500+

lower than population levels in areas where the primary infected species
were foxes and skunks, respectively (Parker 1962:274). Discreteness of
enzootic fox- and skunk-rabies areas may possibly be explained by a
combination of factors — lower susceptibility of one species to virus
maintained primarily by the other species, ecological and behavioral
isolation of the species, and differences in continuity of populations
from one area to another.

Skunks infected with rabies are most frequently reported in the
North Central States, Texas, and California (Fig. 51). In the Midwest, distribution of rabies in skunks appears to conform fairly closely
with distribution of corn-producing areas (Martin and Leonard 1949:
332, Fig. 88). The preference, exhibited by skunks, for cornfield habitats may indicate that the correlation is real.

Public health agencies that compile statistics concerning rabies in wild mammals usually do not distinguish between various species of skunks (Scholtens, personal communication). Johnson (1959:423) stated that during epidemics of rabies in skunks, the striped skunk was the species most commonly infected, but added that "this may be more apparent than real, because this skunk is more closely associated with human habitation, as compared with the small spotted skunk, *Spilogale*

Fig. 50. Numbers of cases of rabies reported in all species of wildlife, in foxes, and in skunks in the United States each year, 1958–62. Adapted from data from the Communicable Disease Center (1963a:3).

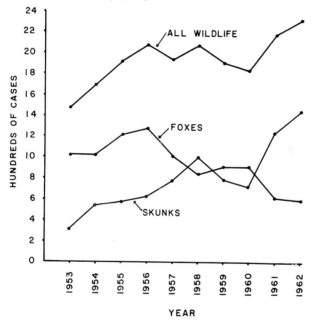

putorius." The latter statement is not in accord with the findings of Crabb (1948:215, Fig. 28), who reported that 73.4 percent of the dens of spotted skunks in Iowa were in or near farm buildings. Furthermore, spotted skunks are not known to occur in Illinois, Ohio, and Michigan, and have been infrequently recorded in peripheral areas of Indiana and Wisconsin (Hall and Kelson 1959:930, Map 472). Thus it was impossible for this species to have been implicated in the epizootic of skunk rabies that prevailed in those parts of the Midwest.

EPIZOOTIOLOGY

The wide range of host species susceptible to rabies, the unique method of dissemination of the disease, and the high rate of mortality among infected individuals indicate that the means by which the disease perpetuates itself are complex. Rabies has been demonstrated repeatedly to be a density-dependent disease; prevalence is directly related to the density of susceptible hosts (Schoening 1956:201). Thus, during epizootics no special mechanisms are required to explain maintenance of the disease, but during interepizootic periods it is difficult to account for the origin of sporadic cases of rabies. Scatterday *et al.* (1960:945-

Fig. 51. Distribution of rabies in skunks in the United States, based on the average number of cases reported in each state, 1961–62. Adapted from data from the Communicable Disease Center (1962:4 and 1963a:9).

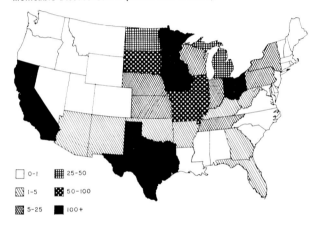

946) proposed three possible explanations for sporadic rabies among wild and domestic carnivores in Florida:

1. A primary reservoir in bats or other small mammals infecting carnivores directly;

2. Enzootic rabies among species recognized to be occasionally involved in epizootics;

3. A multispecies complex.

A reservoir species, to be effective in perpetuating the virus, must possess some mechanism by which the virus can be maintained for relatively long periods, longer than normal incubation and symptomatic periods. Pawan (1936:401-422) demonstrated that vampire bats in Central and South America were asymptomatic carriers of the disease and could transmit the virus over extended periods. Although a reservoir of this type helps to explain the maintenance of the disease during interepizootic periods, a reservoir need not be synonymous with an asymptomatic "typhoid-Mary" type of carrier, nor is it necessary to assume that all individuals of a reservoir species possess the mechanism to maintain the virus, nor that a reservoir be a relatively obscure species not ordinarily involved in epizootics.

The concept of a multispecies complex for maintaining the virus during interepizootic periods appears to create as many questions as it solves. Many cases of rabies reported during interepizootic periods are in species which are sharply separated ecologically and behaviorally. These factors would probably severely limit opportunities for transfer of virus between them. In addition, there is evidence that virus maintained within a single species for several passages becomes progressively less virulent for other species. Occasional passage of virus from reservoir species, through ecological and behavioral barriers, to other species would explain occurrence of rabies in species sporadically infected, without further complicating an already complex situation.

Nevertheless, in evaluating the role of any species of mammal in the epizootiology of rabies, either as a potential reservoir or as a species infected from a reservoir species, each of the three concepts discussed above must be considered for the species in question and for associated species.

Livestock

Although natural transmission of rabies from an infected bovine or equine to a dog, skunk, or fox by biting is not impossible, such occurrences must be exceedingly rare. For this reason, farm animals may be disregarded as potential sources of infection, except perhaps for other livestock and for animal husbandmen. The primary sources of the disease in livestock appear to be in both wild and domestic carnivores. When considered separately, there does not appear to be a correlation between the reported incidence of rabies in livestock and the reported incidence in wild carnivores or in domestic carnivores. However, the peak in reported incidence of rabies in livestock occurred during the late 1940's and early 1950's (Fig. 52), prior to effective control of rabies in domestic carnivores and after the beginning of the epizootic of rabies in wildlife (Fig. 48).

Bats

Rabies in chiropterans has been known for more than half a century (Martin 1959:6), but rabies was not discovered among insectivorous bats in the United States until 1953 (Venters et al. 1954:18). Since

that time rabies has been reported in bats from 38 states (Communicable Disease Center 1963b:1). While the exact role of insectivorous
bats in the epizootiology of the disease is not clearly understood, the
mobility of these forms makes possible the rapid dispersal of the disease over wide areas. However, the probability of transmission of
rabies from bats to terrestrial species appears to be slight. Tierkel

Fig. 52. Numbers of cases of rabies reported in domestic livestock in the United States
each year, 1938–62. Adapted from data from the Communicable Disease Center (1961:8
and 1963a:3).

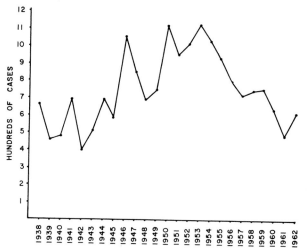

(1959:201) cited evidence showing that it is often difficult to infect
terrestrial species with virus isolated from rabid bats. In addition, the
relatively short teeth of bats seem incapable of creating wounds in long-
furred, tough-skinned terrestrial mammals. Skunks and other species
of terrestrial mammals are known to eat bats (Sperry 1933:152-153,
Goodpaster and Hoffmeister 1950:457). Although acquisition of rabies
by ingestion of infected tissue is possible, the possibility of bites on the
lips, gums, or tongue, or of transmission through abrasions in the mouth
while eating bats, appears to be considerably greater. However, the
rate of mortality among mice fed infected tissue was not significantly
increased by artificially induced oral wounds (Soave 1966:45-46). The
conditions apparently necessary for aerosol transmission of rabies probably occur too rarely for this mode of transmission to be of epizootiological significance. In northwestern Illinois, the common species of
bats did not appear to be infected with rabies (Verts and Barr 1961:

384-387). Because of the low incidence of rabies in bats and the apparent lack of intimate association with skunks, bats were not believed to be reservoirs of rabies from which skunks became infected.

Foxes

Discreteness of skunk-rabies areas and fox-rabies areas, and resistance exhibited by skunks to rabies virus isolated from foxes, tend to indicate that rabies is not often passed back and forth between these species. There was evidence that foxes were not involved in the 1961-62 outbreak of rabies in skunks in northwestern Illinois (Verts and Storm 1966:419-421), although 5 of 36 red foxes had significant SN antibody levels in their sera (Table 29).

Raccoons

Raccoons are reported to be relatively frequently infected with rabies in peninsular Florida, but their role in the epizootiology of wildlife rabies in that area is unclear because of their unaggressive behavior when infected (Scatterday et al. 1960:950-951). Relatively few rabid raccoons are reported in the remainder of the United States; only 23 were reported in Illinois between 1940 and 1962. In northwestern Illinois, none of 214 raccoons collected between December 1957 and April 1959 contained virus in their brains or salivary glands. Additional raccoons were not tested for presence of rabies virus during the 1961–62 rabies epizootic in skunks, but only three rabid raccoons were reported in Illinois during this outbreak, none from the northwestern part of the state. Raccoons apparently were not reservoirs of rabies during the interepizootic period preceding outbreak of the disease in skunks.

Opossums

Opossums are rarely reported to be infected with rabies; only four rabid opossums were reported in Illinois between 1940 and 1962. Gier (1948:145) believed that the disease did not become epizootic among opossums. Beamer et al. (1960:510) presented experimental evidence that opossums were highly resistant to rabies. None of 132 opossums collected between January and September, 1958 had rabies virus in their brains or salivary glands. None of 143 serum samples contained significant levels of SN antibodies (Table 29).

Table 29. Results of tests for rabies-neutralizing antibodies on serum samples collected from wild mammals during an interepizootic period, northwestern Illinois, January 1, 1958–December 31, 1960. Samples were tested by means of screening tests against 12.6 to 50.1 mouse LD_{50} of virus.*

SPECIES	TOTAL NUMBER TESTED	0/6	1/6	2/6	3/6	4/6	5/6	6/6
Mephitis mephitis	120	92	21	5†	1	1	–	–
Didelphis marsupialis	143	135	8	–	–	–	–	–
Vulpes fulva	36	24	5	2	1	1	3	–
Mustela vison	7	4	1	–	1	–	1	–
Mustela frenata	6	4	2	–	–	–	–	–
Mustela rixosa	1	1	–	–	–	–	–	–
Totals	313	260	37	7	3	2	4	–

NUMBERS OF SERA TESTED DISTRIBUTED ACCORDING TO PROPORTIONS OF MICE PROTECTED/INOCULATED IN EACH CASE

* Antibody level considered significant when at least half of the mice were protected.
† Includes 1 rabid animal.

Minks and Weasels

Minks and weasels are rarely reported to be infected with rabies, but Johnson (1960:271-274) implied that their role in the epizootiology of rabies may be more important than indicated by the reported incidence among them. No minks or weasels were reported to be infected with rabies in Illinois between 1940 and 1962. None of 31 minks and 12 long-tailed and least weasels caught in northwestern Illinois between 1957 and 1960 was infected, but 2 of 7 minks had significant SN antibody levels in their blood serum (Table 29). The normal semiaquatic nature of minks and the usual avoidance of lowland habitats exhibited by striped skunks suggest that the two species were separated ecologically. Although weasels were associated with striped skunks in some habitats in northwestern Illinois, their irregular distribution and low numbers tended to indicate that weasels were not involved in the 1961–62 epizootic of rabies in striped skunks.

Badgers

Badgers are rarely reported to be infected with rabies; only one rabid badger was reported in Illinois between 1940 and 1962. One badger, caught in northwestern Illinois in 1959, was not infected. The close ecological relationship between badgers and striped skunks suggests that there may be many opportunities for exchange of rabies virus between these species, but the scarcity of badgers and their limited range in Illinois (Hoffmeister and Mohr 1957:111) tended to indicate that they were not important disseminators of the disease.

Small Mammals

Small mammals (shrews, mice, voles, and ground squirrels) are rarely reported to be infected with rabies. None of over 1,000 rodents collected from high enzootic and epizootic areas in New York and Georgia was infected (Tierkel 1959:198). Most of these species are delicate creatures which would probably rarely recover from the bite of a carnivore. Verts and Barr (1960:438) and Pearson and Barr (1962: 35-37) found no evidence of a reservoir of rabies among shrews in Illinois.

Skunks

Because no other species of mammal appeared to be greatly involved in the epizootic of rabies in striped skunks in northwestern Illinois in 1961–62, skunks alone apparently were responsible for the epizootic. Two possible sources of the infection remain to be considered:

1. The infection moved to that part of the state, step by step, through existing skunk populations from some other geographical area.

2. Skunks in that part of the state maintained the virus in an inactive form until conditions necessary for outbreak of the disease occurred.

REPORTED RABIES IN STRIPED SKUNKS IN ILLINOIS

Records obtained from the Division of Livestock Industry, Illinois Department of Agriculture, indicated that rabies in striped skunks was reported in Illinois at least as early as 1940. During the 1940's, the relatively few cases of rabies reported in skunks were widely scattered in time (Table 30) and space (Fig. 53). Most cases of rabies reported during that decade were in dogs; most occurred during intense epizootics in metropolitan areas.

During the 1950's, the average number of cases of rabies reported in striped skunks in Illinois annually was more than 10 times the average annual rate during the previous decade (Table 30). Despite this relatively large increase in the reported incidence of the disease in skunks, the only significant concentration of rabid skunks occurred in 1957, 1958, and 1959 in Jefferson County in south-central Illinois (Fig. 53). This focus of skunk rabies may have been more apparent than real; factors other than actual prevalence of rabies in skunks may have in-

Table 30. *Reported incidence of rabies in animals in Illinois, 1940–62.* Data are from Division of Animal Industries, Illinois Department of Agriculture.

| | | | | | OTHER | LIVE- | | |
YEAR	DOGS	CATS	SKUNKS	FOXES	WILDLIFE	STOCK	HUMAN	TOTALS
1940	281	8	2	–	1	7	–	299
1941	321	13	–	1	2	5	–	342
1942	282	13	1	1	1	3	–	301
1943	342	30	1	–	–	9	–	382
1944	393	38	1	1	1	12	–	446
1945	409	54	2	2	5	13	–	485
1946	315	34	–	4	3	13	1	370
1947	171	9	2	3	1	8	–	194
1948	135	11	–	2	–	3	–	151
1949	102	26	4	4	6	26	–	168
1950	110	45	10	13	6	34	–	218
1951	127	22	5	9	4	22	–	189
1952	322	25	8	5	5	18	–	383
1953	107	10	4	12	6	13	–	152
1954	205	18	10	7	4	11	1	256
1955	41	8	15	4	1	15	–	84
1956	59	12	20	4	3	14	–	112
1957	21	12	31	2	8	15	–	89
1958	9	3	24	4	3	18	–	61
1959	7	9	21	5	4	11	–	57
1960	9	13	31	6	5	20	–	84
1961	12	11	95	11	3	29	–	161
1962	7	12	74	9	8	29	–	139

fluenced the reported incidence of the disease among them. In 1958, while discussing this apparent epizootic with several veterinarians in Jefferson County, I was impressed by their obvious zeal in submitting suspected rabid animals to state laboratories for testing. In other areas of Illinois, where there was less public interest in this zoonosis, I knew of several cases in which animals with symptoms of rabies were not submitted to state laboratories for testing because they had not bitten a domestic animal or a human.

During the first 3 years of the 1960's, the average annual rate of reported rabies in striped skunks in Illinois was 4.5 times greater than during the previous decade, and more than 50 times greater than during the 1940's (Table 30). Nearly half of the reported cases occurred in the northern third of the state during the early 1960's (Fig. 53).

During this span of 23 years for which data were available, factors other than actual prevalence of the disease among striped skunks may have been involved in the increase in the reported incidence of rabies among them. Both the general public and public health agencies became increasingly interested in rabies, particularly rabies in wildlife. This increased interest may have been partly responsible for the increase in reported incidence of rabies in skunks. However, the rapidity with which the greatest increase occurred (Table 30) and the size of the area over which rabies in skunks was reported (Fig. 53) tended to

Fig. 53. Numbers of cases of rabies reported in striped skunks in Illinois, by county. *Left, 1940–49; center, 1950–59; right, 1960–62.*

indicate that enhanced interest was not wholly responsible for the increase in reported incidence of the disease in skunks.

These data also indicated that rabies in striped skunks was endemic in Illinois for a long period of time prior to the epizootic in northern Illinois during the early 1960's. Although some adjoining states (particularly Iowa and Wisconsin) reported relatively large numbers of rabid skunks annually prior to the outbreak in northern Illinois, the wide distribution of rabies in skunks in Illinois during the 1950's (Fig. 53) does not justify the conclusion that the epizootic was caused by spread of the disease from other states.

The slow increase of reported rabies in skunks during the 1950's and the sudden increase in the early 1960's tended to indicate that some change in the skunk population (numbers, distribution, behavior, etc.) was involved in the increase in rabies among them.

SEASONAL CHANGES IN INCIDENCE OF RABIES IN STRIPED SKUNKS

Data provided by the Division of Livestock Industry, Illinois Department of Agriculture, and by the Public Health Veterinarian, Iowa

State Department of Health, indicated that the incidence of rabies reported in skunks was correlated with season. Of 1,746 cases of rabies reported in skunks in Iowa between 1949 and 1962, 629 (36.0 percent) occurred during the second quarter of the year (April–June), and of 245 cases of rabies reported in skunks in Illinois between 1958 and 1962, 90 (36.7 percent) occurred during the same period. In Iowa and Illinois, the peak number of cases of rabies reported in skunks occurred during the second quarter in 10 of 14 years and in 3 of 5 years, respectively (Fig. 54).

Fig. 54. Numbers of cases of rabies reported in striped skunks each quarter in Iowa, 1949–62, and Illinois, 1958–62. Extended marks on abscissa denote second quarter of each year.

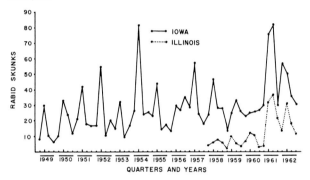

In Iowa, the peak in the mean monthly number of cases of rabies reported in skunks occurred in April, with June and May having the next highest averages, respectively (Fig. 55). In Illinois, the peak in the mean monthly number of cases occurred in July (Fig. 55), but more than half the cases reported during that month occurred in a single year (1961). Data from Iowa may be more reliable than those from Illinois because of the larger sample and the longer sampling period. Parker (1962:276) reported that peaks in numbers of reported cases of rabies in skunks in the North Central States between 1957 and 1960, and in Wisconsin between 1953 and 1957, occurred in April and July. Unfortunately, he presented no data; the relative heights of the peaks could not be compared.

PREVALENCE OF RABIES IN STRIPED SKUNKS IN NORTHWESTERN ILLINOIS, 1958–62

During the course of the present investigation, brain and salivary gland tissues from 251 striped skunks collected in Jo Daviess, Stephenson, Carroll, and Whiteside counties were tested for presence of rabies virus. The testing procedure was the mouse inoculation test described by Koprowski (1954:56-68), with slight modifications (Verts and Barr

Fig. 55. Seasonal incidence of rabies in striped skunks, revealed by mean numbers of rabid striped skunks reported each month in Iowa and Illinois.

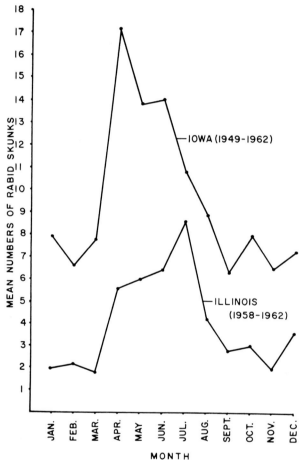

1960:438). Numbers of striped skunks tested and numbers of skunks with rabies virus in their brains or salivary glands, or in both, each month between January 1958 and August 1962 are shown in Table 31.

Of 122 striped skunks caught prior to September 30, 1960, none was infected with rabies. (The established policy of the project was not to

Table 31. Numbers of brain and of salivary gland tissues from striped skunks collected each month, and numbers of striped skunks infected with rabies each month, northwestern Illinois, 1958–62. Numbers of rabid skunks are shown in parentheses.

MONTH	1958	1959	1960	1961	1962	TOTALS
January	–	–	1	1	–	2
February	–	–	1	10	–	11
March	2	–	5	2	–	9
April	–	–	7	6 (4)	12 (4)	25 (8)
May	2	–	9	7 (3)	12 (1)	30 (4)
June	11	–	3	5 (3)	8 (1)	27 (4)
July	10	–	6	–	10	26
August	6	–	3	4	17 (1)	30 (1)
September	15	–	2	2 (1)	–	19 (1)
October	21	–	27 (1)	2	–	50 (1)
November	15	–	3 (1)	1	–	19 (1)
December	2	1	–	–	–	3
Totals	84	1	67 (2)	40 (11)	59 (7)	251 (20)

kill skunks for testing during 1959.) Of 124 striped skunks caught after October 1, 1960, 20 (16.1 percent) were rabid. The time at which this change occurred corresponded closely with the time that the increase in numbers of rabid skunks occurred, as reported by the Division of Livestock Industry, Illinois Department of Agriculture.

Seasonal Changes in Prevalence of Rabies

Of the 20 rabid striped skunks caught in northwestern Illinois between October 1960 and August 1962, 16 (80.0 percent) were captured during the second quarter of the year, 8 (40.0 percent) during the month of April (Table 31). The monthly distribution of rabid skunks was significantly different from that expected on the basis of the monthly distribution of all skunks captured ($P < 0.01$).

SEX RATIOS OF INFECTED AND OF NONINFECTED STRIPED SKUNKS

Of the 20 rabid striped skunks caught in northwestern Illinois, 19 (95.0 percent) were females. During April, May, and June, 1961 and 1962 combined, 49 striped skunks (23 males and 26 females) were caught, of which 16 (1 male and 15 females) were rabid. Chi-square tests indicated that sex ratios of rabid and of nonrabid skunks were significantly different ($P < 0.01$).

To obtain additional data concerning sex ratios of rabid skunks, state laboratories in Illinois and Iowa were requested to record the sex of each rabid skunk tested between October 1961 and October 1962. Of 140 rabid skunks reported by the laboratories, the sex of only 11 was determined — 6 males and 5 females; in most cases only heads of suspected animals were submitted. Differences in seasonal distribution of the two sexes of rabid skunks may be significant: five of six males were reported in December, January, or February, whereas only one of five females was reported during those months.

AGES OF RABID STRIPED SKUNKS

Ages of 19 rabid striped skunks caught in northwestern Illinois were estimated by the lens-weight technique. Ten (52.6 percent) of these skunks were less than 12 months old. Thirteen (81.3 percent) of 16 rabid skunks caught in April, May, and June were born during the previous year. These age ratios do not appear to be greatly different from those that probably existed for the population as a whole.

In an attempt to accumulate more information concerning ages of rabid striped skunks, state testing laboratories in Iowa and Illinois were requested to preserve in 10 percent formalin the eyes from rabid skunks. Eyes which could be used for estimating ages were obtained from 109 striped skunks; unfortunately, the seasonal distribution of these collections was not uniform, mostly because about 30 eyes from rabid skunks were destroyed during shipment from one of the laboratories during the summer months. Of 45 rabid skunks submitted to the laboratories between September and December, 1961, only 9 (20.0 percent) were more than 12 months old, but of 60 rabid skunks submitted between January and April, 1962, 28 (46.7 percent) were older than 12 months. These differences cannot be explained on the bases of known changes in age ratios among striped skunk populations.

DISTRIBUTIONS OF RABID AND NONRABID STRIPED SKUNKS IN CARROLL COUNTY, ILLINOIS

Analyses of distributions of rabid and nonrabid striped skunks were based entirely on data collected in Carroll County, Illinois. Data collected in other areas were excluded because 202 (80.5 percent) of the 251 striped skunks tested for rabies, and 17 (85.0 percent) of the 20 rabid skunks caught, were obtained in Carroll County; other captures were made in widely scattered parts of Jo Daviess, Stephenson, and Whiteside counties.

Tissues from 81 striped skunks caught in Carroll County between January 1958 and September 1960 were tested for presence of rabies virus; none was infected. Distribution of sites of capture of skunks tested during this period was fairly uniform throughout the county (Fig. 56). Of these 81 skunks, 34 (42.0 percent) were caught within 2 miles of one or more sites where rabid skunks were caught subsequently.

Fig. 56. Distribution of capture sites of 81 striped skunks caught in Carroll County, Illinois, January, 1958–September, 1960. None was rabid.

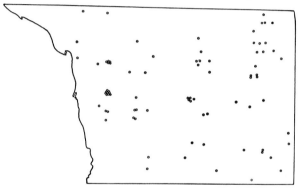

Sixty-five striped skunks caught in Carroll County between October 1960 and December 1961 were tested for rabies; 12 were infected. Distribution of these 65 captures was considerably less uniform than the distribution of the sample caught prior to outbreak of the epizootic of rabies among skunks (Fig. 57). The distribution of capture sites of rabid skunks was, in general, more restricted than the distribution of all captures. Three areas, each less than 4 miles in diameter, contained nine (75.0 percent) of the rabid skunks caught during this period.

Fifty-six striped skunks caught in Carroll County between January and August, 1962, were tested for rabies; five were infected. Distribution of these 56 captures was restricted mostly to the eastern half of the county (Fig. 58). Distribution of rabid skunks in the county was, in general, similar to that observed during the previous period. However, numbers of rabid and nonrabid skunks caught in 1962, within 2 miles of sites of captures of rabid skunks in 1960 and 1961, were not significantly different from numbers of rabid and nonrabid skunks caught in 1962 farther than 2 miles from such sites.

A "moving wave" of rabies infection through striped skunk populations in Carroll County was not evident. After becoming established, rabies appeared to be maintained by skunk populations in local areas for several years. Parker (1962:275) made a similar observation con-

Fig. 57. Distribution of capture sites of 65 striped skunks caught in Carroll County, Illinois, October, 1960–December, 1961. Solid triangles represent sites at which rabid skunks were caught.

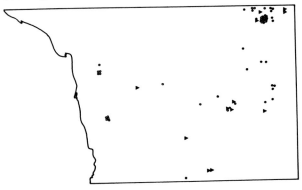

Fig. 58. Distribution of capture sites of 56 striped skunks caught in Carroll County, Illinois, January–August, 1962. Solid triangles represent sites at which rabid skunks were caught.

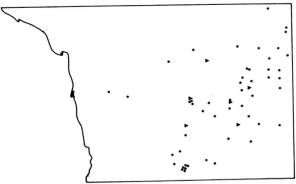

cerning rabies in skunks in an area in south-central Wisconsin. Storm and Verts (1966:705-708) reported that the movements of a striped skunk infected with rabies were not significantly more extensive than those of noninfected skunks of the same sex and of similar ages. Restricted movements, if typical of most rabid skunks, might help to explain the mechanism by which these apparent foci remain more or less discrete.

The data were insufficient to determine if rates of infection decreased in proportion to the distance from the center of the foci of infection. However, skunks infected with rabies were collected within a relatively short period of time over a relatively wide area in Carroll County. This suggests that the disease became established more or less simultaneously in several local areas. A similar observation was made on the reported distribution of rabies in skunks throughout Illinois in 1961.

OTHER CHARACTERISTICS OF RABID STRIPED SKUNKS

Of the 20 striped skunks infected with rabies, nine (45.0 percent) did not have detectable virus in their salivary glands. The infected skunks may have been killed before the salivary glands became infected; however, Sikes (1962:1043-44) found virus in saliva of experimentally infected striped skunks as early as 5 days prior to onset of clinical symptoms and as long as 9 days after onset of symptoms. Data collected in northwestern Illinois tend to indicate that the rate of infectivity among wild striped skunks may be relatively low. No skunk collected had rabies virus in the salivary glands without also having virus in tissues of the central nervous system.

Of the 15 rabid female striped skunks collected in the months of April, May, and June, all were pregnant or lactating. Of the nine pregnant females infected with rabies, two were resorbing embryos; one entire gravidum of seven and one embryo of a gravidum of nine were being resorbed. Of the eight pregnant females infected with rabies for which duration of gestation could be estimated, all had been pregnant for at least 40 days (range 40 to 57 days).

Mean body weight of rabid female striped skunks collected in the months of April, May, and June was 3.82 ± 0.12 lb; that of non-infected females collected at the same season was 4.31 ± 0.19 lb. These means were significantly different $(P < 0.05)$. Whether this difference in weight was a result of the infection or the infection became manifest because of the weight loss is unknown. However, an average weight loss of 11 percent within the few days of the symptomatic period of rabies appears incongruous with an average weight loss of 55 percent during the approximately 90-day fasting period in winter.

BEHAVIOR OF STRIPED SKUNKS INFECTED WITH RABIES

Striped skunks infected with rabies apparently exhibit furious symptoms of the disease more frequently than paralytic symptoms; all five of the naturally infected striped skunks kept in cages exhibited furious symptoms. Richards (1957:4) stated that rabid skunks are "more aggressive and determined" than any other form of wildlife in their attacks on humans and on other animals.

Early in the symptomatic stages of rabies, striped skunks appeared to be lethargic; one young skunk slept for most of 2 days before exhibiting furious symptoms. There was also a loss of appetite, but no hydrophobia was noted. However, when rabid skunks drank, they appeared to bite at the surface of the water rather than lap water as normal skunks do. Rabid skunks observed during this investigation were usually quiet for relatively long periods unless stimulated by movement, strong light, or loud noise. When irritated by these stimuli, striped skunks made strong and persistent attempts to reach the sources of irritation, although the attempts were frequently misdirected. Usually, skunks appeared to become completely exhausted before they ceased their efforts to reach the sources of irritation, often lying on their sides and gasping for several minutes from the exertion.

One unique characteristic of rabies in striped skunks is that the ability of skunks to scent (expel musk) is usually inhibited. Richards (1957:4) reported that 90 percent of the skunks with furious symptoms submitted to the North Dakota Agricultural College for testing did not scent; many did not scent while dying.

Striped skunks are usually considered to be crepuscular or nocturnal; however, when infected with rabies they may be active at any hour. Parker (1962:274) stated that in areas where rabies in skunks is prevalent, sighting a skunk during the daylight hours is "reasonable grounds to suspect the animal of being infected with the disease."

The more subtle changes in behavior of striped skunks caused by rabies, particularly those which might affect the relative ease with which skunks can be caught in traps, were of greatest interest in the present study. These changes are extremely difficult to measure so must be treated subjectively. If the olfactory senses were either inhibited or hypersensitized by rabies infections, traps baited with food or scent or both might be selective of noninfected or of infected skunks, respectively. Observations of noninfected striped skunks in cages and in the wild indicated that their olfactory senses were not acute; there was little indication that food or scent in or near traps increased the effectiveness of the traps. Traps set in natural pathways, such as road culverts, probably tended to bias data on prevalence of rabies among striped skunks less than traps which depended entirely on an olfactory lure to entice skunks to them. Even though most striped skunks exhibited extremely addled behavior throughout most of the symptomatic period, they probably tended to follow natural pathways because of greater ease of travel. However, the confused condition, combined with the lethargy exhibited early in the symptomatic stages, probably resulted in a smaller proportion of infected skunks being caught compared with the proportion of infected skunks in the population.

RELATIONSHIPS BETWEEN LIFE HISTORY EVENTS, POPULATION STRUCTURE, AND PREVALENCE OF RABIES AMONG STRIPED SKUNKS

On the basis of relative numbers of individuals of various species reported to be infected with rabies in the Midwest, striped skunks were "prime suspects" in the search for reservoir-species of the disease. The relatively long history of sporadic cases of rabies among skunks, and the lack of evidence that one or more species transmitted rabies to striped skunks and that a multispecies complex was involved in the perpetuation of the disease, tend to support incrimination of striped skunks as a reservoir-species. If striped skunks are reservoirs of rabies, the means by which the disease is perpetuated among their populations requires explanation.

There was no evidence that striped skunks can become asymptomatic carriers of rabies, capable of directly transmitting the disease by biting; that is, they were not terrestrial counterparts of vampire bats. However, this does not preclude the possibility that individual striped skunks are able to maintain the virus by some other means, or that populations of striped skunks can maintain rabies among themselves through direct transmission by biting.

Because rates of infection of rabies in dogs (particularly in metropolitan areas) have been shown to be density-dependent, a relationship between population levels of striped skunks and prevalence of rabies among them was expected. Changes in prevalence of rabies among striped skunks appeared to be related to changes in numbers of striped skunks (Fig. 59). Peaks in incidence of rabies reported in Illinois and Iowa, and in prevalence of rabies among striped skunks collected in northwestern Illinois, coincided with peaks in population levels of striped skunks, based on the studies conducted in northwestern Illinois

Fig. 59. A comparison between the reported incidence of rabies among striped skunks in Iowa and Illinois, the observed prevalence of rabies among skunks in northwestern Illinois, the relative density of striped skunks in northwestern Illinois, and the proportions of females in samples of striped skunks in northwestern Illinois each year, 1958–62.

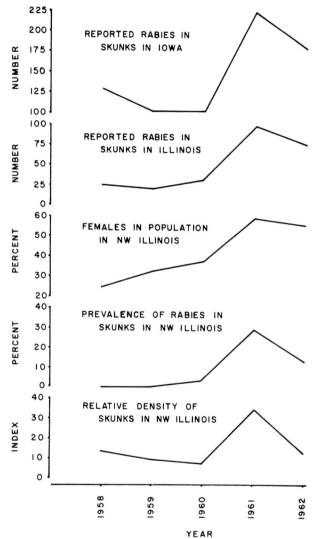

(Fig. 59). There also appeared to be some correlation between numbers of rabid skunks reported and numbers of skunks observed along roadsides in various geographic regions of Illinois and Iowa. If prevalence of rabies were related *only* to density of susceptible hosts, the seasonal peak in prevalence of rabies would be expected to coincide with the seasonal peak in numbers of "independent" skunks; that is, sometime after young skunks become independent of parental care. However, the seasonal peak in prevalence of the disease occurred in April, May, and June, the time at which population levels of striped skunks independent of parental care were at or near the annual low point. This discrepancy, the absence of evidence of "wildfire" spread of the disease through populations of striped skunks, and the apparent persistence of the disease among skunks in localized areas during outbreaks, suggest that epizootics of rabies among striped skunks involve considerably more than a high population level of hosts over a wide area.

The clumped distribution of populations of striped skunks, caused by delayed dispersion of family groups in summer and by gregarious denning habits in winter, would seem to restrict spread of rabies through populations of skunks. During epizootics, groups of skunks forced closer together by pressures of high population levels may be able to support the disease by infected individuals biting noninfected individuals. However, during interepizootic periods, groups of skunks may be so widely spaced that the probability of rabies spreading through the population would appear to be very low. Because of the relatively low rate of infectivity observed among infected skunks, and because of the isolating effect of clumped distributions, it is difficult to believe that "infected individual biting noninfected individual" chains of transmission are wholly responsible for perpetuation of rabies among striped skunk populations during interepizootic periods. Considering that during winter striped skunks frequently spend 3 months or longer in dens, it appears that perpetuation of rabies among skunks by this method of transmission would be severely hampered even during epizootics.

The seasonal peak in prevalence of rabies seemingly would be correlated with the period when the isolating effect of the clumped distribution of populations of striped skunks was at a minimum. Greatest movements, hence the least isolation, appeared to occur during and just after the breeding season. Allowing 30 to 60 days for incubation of the virus, individuals infected with rabies in April, May, and June would seem to have been exposed (bitten) during or shortly after the breeding season. Although movements were usually greatest, and considerable fighting appeared to occur among striped skunks during and just after the breeding season, the peak in prevalence of rabies during the second quarter of the year does not seem to be wholly explainable on these bases. Movements of striped skunks tended to be severely restricted by inclement weather, particularly by deep snow; therefore, prevalence of rabies among striped skunks during the second quarter should be markedly reduced during years when deep snow covers the ground during the breeding season. In Iowa in 1960, when 5 or more inches of snow covered the ground (at Des Moines, Sioux City, and Davenport) continuously from February 10 to March 27 (overlapping the breeding season considerably), 25 cases of rabies in skunks were reported in April, May, and June. In Iowa in 1959, 5 or more inches of snow covered the ground at the same cities for 7 or fewer days between February 10 and March 27, but 25 cases of rabies in skunks also were reported in April, May, and June. Also, weather conditions, particularly depth of snow, did not appear to be markedly less severe in 1961, when the greatest increase in reported incidence of rabies in skunks occurred during the second quarter of the year, than in 1958 or 1959, when the reported incidence of rabies in skunks was nearer the long-time average.

Although population levels and distribution of striped skunks appear to be factors involved in the epizootiology of rabies among them, particularly during epizootics, they do little to explain the mechanisms by which rabies is maintained by striped skunk populations during interepizootic periods. During interepizootic periods, a combination of low rates of infectivity among infected skunks, low population levels, and grouped distribution of skunk populations appears to be an insurmountable obstacle to perpetuation of rabies in skunk populations through transmission of the virus by biting. Numerous cases of rabies in striped skunks, reported sporadically in time and space, are strong evidence that the species is a reservoir of the disease. This leads to the suspicion that other methods, either by themselves or in addition to transmission by biting, may be the means by which rabies is perpetuated among striped skunks.

There was a marked difference in prevalence of rabies between sexes of striped skunks during the seasonal peak in prevalence of the disease in April, May, and June; females were infected 15 times more frequently than males, in samples collected in northwestern Illinois. There was also some evidence, based on a small sample collected by public health laboratories, that in winter the prevalence of rabies among male skunks was higher than among female skunks. During copulation or attempted copulation, females were almost invariably bitten by males, but females often reciprocated, particularly if they were not receptive.

Also, there appeared to be considerable fighting among males during the breeding season. Although rabid skunks of both sexes were usually aggressive and vicious, they were probably so addled by the disease that mating drives were suppressed. Thus, there is no reason to believe that transmission of rabies by biting was almost always from male to female. This tends to indicate that female striped skunks were subjected to different conditions or responded differently from males to the same conditions. During the seasonal peak in prevalence of rabies among striped skunks the most obvious difference between the two sexes was that females were pregnant or lactating. In addition, females lost a greater proportion of their autumn body weights during winter and recovered their weight losses in spring more slowly than males. Stresses associated with pregnancy and lactation, coupled with stresses associated with loss of body weight during the period of winter dormancy, may be involved in the difference in the prevalence of rabies between the sexes at this season.

Changes in prevalence of rabies among striped skunks appeared to be related to changes in their sex ratios (Fig. 59). During the interepizootic period (1958–60), there was a preponderance of males in samples of adult striped skunks collected in northwestern Illinois. Because observed sex ratios of many species of mammals frequently favor males, the preponderance of males in the samples was not considered abnormal, even though proportions of females in the samples were lower than expected. During the epizootic of rabies among striped skunks in 1961 and 1962, females predominated among samples of adult striped skunks collected in northwestern Illinois. This is an unusual situation among populations of wild mammals, particularly when differences in rates of infection of rabies between sexes, observed among the samples, are considered. The proportion of females among the sample of juveniles collected in summer in 1960 indicated that the "shift" toward a predominately female population began several months prior to outbreak of rabies. Whether or not observed changes in sex ratios of striped skunks betweeen years and between age-classes represent results of differential mortality between sexes, caused by rabies, is unknown.

If rabies is at least partly responsible for changes in sex ratios, it is possible to speculate, from this basis, on mechanisms by which rabies may be perpetuated among populations of striped skunks. Because the rate of infection observed among adult females during pregnancy and lactation was considerably higher than among other sex- and age-classes at other seasons, one of the most significant links in the nebulous chain of transmission may be from adult females to their offspring. This might occur in several ways: (1) transmission at birth when the umbilical cord is bitten. Johnson (1960:273), in a discussion of rabies in spotted skunks, rejected this hypothesis because of the presumed neurotropic nature of rabies virus and the "lack of nervous tissue in the umbilical cord." Even more important, presence of rabies virus in the central nervous system of all striped skunks with virus in their salivary glands would indicate that the adult female probably would succumb to the disease long before the young were weaned. Death of the young from starvation would break the chain of transmission. (2) Johnson (1960:273) suggested that young skunks might become infected with rabies virus from the milk of their mothers. If this occurred late in lactation, or if virus occurred in milk of asymptomatic females, it might be possible for the young to survive to exhibit symptoms weeks or months later. If infection of the mammary glands were accompanied by infection of the central nervous system, as I suspect that it is, successful transmission through milk to the offspring would be dependent on the timing of the onset of infection in the adult female to coincide with weaning. There were no indications that onset of symptoms was delayed until just before weaning of the young; in fact, symptoms occurred more frequently among pregnant animals than among lactating animals. (3) Latent infections in adult females might be transmitted to young as latent infections. Adult females with active rabies acquired from bites during the breeding season or through reactivation of latent rabies would then be involved in perpetuation of the disease only to the extent of transmitting the virus to other adults or to their young (if, by chance, weaning coincided with onset of symptoms) by biting. Latent infections in the young might remain inactive until the animals were subjected to unusual stresses.

Experimental evidence of latency and *in utero* transmission of rabies virus is weak; therefore, the preceding suggestion (3) may appear to be quite bold. Konradi (1916:37-46) believed that the infectious material of rabies could be transmitted from the mother to the foetus but that in the process the virus was modified. Remlinger (1919:378) found rabies virus in the brain of an embryo guinea pig whose mother died of the disease. He also reported (pp. 380-381) that a female guinea pig inoculated with rabies virus died 122 days postinoculation, 38 days after her offspring died of the same disease. Sims *et al.* (1963: 25) demonstrated *in utero* transmission of rabies virus in bats. However, evidence of *in utero* transmission of rabies virus in terrestrial species, subsequent to the early reports cited, is lacking, and later reports have indicated that the placenta acts as a barrier to the transfer of the virus from mother to foetus (Sims *et al.* 1963:25, Viazhevich 1957: 1022-23).

Certainly no new principle of viral transmission is proposed. Viruses of swine influenza (Smith 1950:17), lymphocytic choriomeningitis in mice, Theiler's mouse encephalomyelitis, herpes simplex in man (Rhodes and van Rooyen 1962:80-81), some viral diseases of fowls, some tumor viruses (Smith 1963:18), and rabies virus (Koprowski 1952:963) are among those known or suspected of causing latent infections. Also, viruses of variola, varicella, Rift Valley fever, rinderpest (Smith 1950:8), lymphocytic choriomeningitis in mice (Rhodes and van Rooyen 1962:81), rubella, and poliomyelitis (Downie 1963:123) are among those known to be transmitted *in utero.* The virus causing lymphocytic choriomeningitis in mice is transmitted *in utero* to offspring which then become carriers of the virus without production of antibodies (Rhodes and van Rooyen 1962:81). The latter authors also believed that reactivation of latent herpes simplex infections "may be precipitated by endocrine, nutritional, or traumatic factors, or by feverish illnesses" (p. 81).

Latent rabies virus, transmitted *in utero,* might become reactivated at different seasons in the two sexes of striped skunks. Although a shift in the sex ratio toward a larger proportion of females appeared to occur prior to weaning, it is difficult to believe that reactivation of rabies among males could be greater than among females in this age group; it is unlikely that males were subjected to greater environmental stress than females prior to weaning. However, young male striped skunks begin to become sexually active in December, about 3 months before females become sexually active. Males of some species (Jordan 1953:307) have less resistance to starvation than females, although they lose a smaller proportion of their body weight; stress effects of malnutrition might occur earlier in winter among males than among females. These environmental stresses may be sufficient to cause reactivation of latent rabies earlier among males than among females, accounting, in part, for the larger number of infected males than infected females observed in winter and the larger proportion of females in the population in April, May, and June.

Reactivation of latent rabies among one or more individuals within separated groups of skunks would account for the relatively widely distributed sporadic cases of rabies among striped skunks during interepizootic periods. Undoubtedly, certain individual striped skunks from time to time are subjected to stresses of greater intensity than are experienced by most of the other individuals in the population. The stresses might reactivate rabies among individuals harboring latent infections; the virus then might be directly transmitted to other individuals in the group by biting. Within small groups, the disease should rapidly "run its course and die out" because of depletion of susceptible hosts. An "inexplicable sporadic case of rabies among striped skunks" would result from the diagnosis of the disease in one of the infected animals in this group.

Admittedly, much of the foregoing discussion of possible mechanisms by which rabies may be perpetuated among populations of striped skunks is based on speculation. However, observations and data recorded in this report strongly suggest that what have been considered fundamental principles of the epizootiology of rabies deserve critical re-evaluation. The following statement by Wilson Smith (1963:20), while not intended to be restricted to any one viral disease, is emphasized for rabies by the present investigation.

In the wider context of transmission from community to community and from country to country, epidemiological behaviour is closely linked with the mechanisms of persistence and latency already discussed, about which far too little is yet known. The geographical distributions of various diseases, the sudden inexplicable appearances of viruses in areas far removed from endemic foci of infection, the sweep of pandemics round the world, the simultaneous outbreaks in several centres of population, etc., all present puzzles which demand for their solution further exploration of virus behaviour at the levels of individual host and susceptible cells.[1]

---

[1] Reprinted from *Mechanisms of Virus Infection*, page 20; Editor: Wilson Smith; published by Academic Press, Inc., New York, N.Y.

LITERATURE CITED

Albert, A. 1961. The mammalian testis. Pages 305-365. *In* W. C. Young (Editor), Sex and internal secretions. Vol. 1. 3rd ed. The Williams & Wilkins Co., Baltimore. xxiv + 704 pp.

Aldrich, T. B. 1896. A chemical study of the secretion of the anal glands of *Mephitis mephitica* (common skunk), with remarks on the physiological properties of this secretion. J. Exptl. Med. 1:323-340.

Allen, D. L. 1939. Winter habits of Michigan skunks. J. Wildl. Mgmt. 3(3):212-228.

————. 1952. Fur bearer or for worse. Field & Stream 56(12):42-43, 134-137.

————, and W. W. Shapton. 1942. An ecological study of winter dens, with special reference to the eastern skunk. Ecology 23(1):59-68.

Allen, R., and W. T. Neill. 1955. The striped skunk. Florida Wildl. 9(4): 6, 42.

Allison, R. 1953. North Carolina gray squirrel investigations, 1947-1950. Final Rept. Project N. C. 26-R, North Carolina Wildl. Resources Comm. 61 pp.

Almeida, J. D., A. F. Howatson, L. Pinteric, and P. Fenje. 1962. Electron microscope observations on rabies virus by negative staining. Virology 18(1):147-151.

American Ornithologists' Union. 1957. Check-list of North American birds. 5th ed. The Lord Baltimore Press, Inc., Baltimore, Maryland. xiii + 691 pp.

Asdell, S. A. 1946. Patterns of mammalian reproduction. Comstock Publishing Co., Inc., Ithaca, New York. x + 437 pp.

Ashbrook, F. G. 1928. Fur-farming for profit. The Macmillan Company, New York. xxiii + 300 pp.

Atanasiu, P., M. Bahmanyar, M. Baltazard, J. P. Fox, K. Habel, M. M. Kaplan, R. E. Kissling, A. Komarov, H. Koprowski, P. Lépine, F. P. Gallardo, and M. Schaeffer. 1956. Rabies neutralizing antibody response to different schedules of serum and vaccine inoculations in non-exposed persons. Bull. World Health Organization 14(4):593-611.

Austin, W. E. 1922. Principles and practice of fur dressing and fur dyeing. D. Van Nostrand Company, New York. vi + 191 pp.

Babero, B. B. 1960. A survey of parasitism in skunks (*Mephitis mephitis*) in Louisiana, with observations on pathological damages due to helminthiasis. J. Parasitol. 46(5, sect. 2, suppl.):26-27. (Abstract.)

Bachrach, M. 1953. Fur. A practical treatise. 3rd ed. Prentice-Hall, Inc., New York. xii + 660 pp.

Bangs, O. 1896. The skunks of the genus *Mephitis* of eastern North America. Proc. Biol. Soc. Washington 10:139-144.

Barr, T. R. B. 1961. Experimental rabies in the opossum (*Didelphis marsupialis virginiana* Kerr). Ph.D. Thesis. Univ. Illinois, Urbana. 83 pp.

Beale, D. M. 1962. Growth of the eye lens in relation to age in fox squirrels. J. Wildl. Mgmt. 26(2):208-211.

Beamer, P. D., C. O. Mohr, and T. R. B. Barr. 1960. Resistance of the opossum to rabies virus. Am. J. Vet. Research 21(82):507-510.

Beamer, R. H., L. R. Penner, and C. W. Hibbard. 1943. Some notes on the biology of the pack rat cuterebrid (*Cuterebrid* [sic] *beameri* Hall) in Kansas. J. Kansas Entomol. Soc. 16(2):47-50.

Bell, J. F., W. Burgdorfer, and G. J. Moore. 1957. The behavior of rabies virus in ticks. J. Infect. Diseases 100(3):278-283.

Bennitt, R., and W. O. Nagel. 1937. A survey of the resident game and fur-bearers of Missouri. Univ. Missouri Studies 12(2):1-215.

Bent, A. C. 1938. Life histories of North American birds of prey. Part 2. U. S. Natl. Museum Bull. 170. viii + 482 pp.

Benton, A. H., and R. H. Cerwonka. 1960. Host relationships of some eastern Siphonaptera. Am. Midland Naturalist 63(2):383-391.

Beule, J. D. 1941 (1940). Cottontail nesting–study in Pennsylvania. Trans. N. Am. Wildl. Conf. 5:320-328.

Bolin, F. M., Jenny Turn, S. H. Richards, and D. F. Eveleth. 1955. Listeriosis of a skunk. Smelly *Mephitis* is carrier of diseases which affect our domestic animals. North Dakota Agr. Expt. Sta. Bimonthly Bull. 18(2):49-50.

Borodina, T. A. 1959. A study on viraemia in experimental rabies. Problems of Virology 4(2):96-100. Translated by F. S. Freisinger from Vopr. Virusol. 2:226-228, 1959.

Bourke, J. G. 1894. Popular medicine, customs, and superstitions of the Rio Grande. J. Am. Folk-lore 7(25):119-146.

Brigham, G. D. 1938. Susceptibility of animals to endemic typhus virus. (Second report.) Public Health Rept. 53(47):2078-79.

Brooke, Marion M., Lois Norman, Dorothy Allain, and G. W. Gorman. 1957. Isolation of *Trypanosoma cruzi*–like organisms from wild animals collected in Georgia. J. Parasitol. 43(5, sect. 2, suppl.):15. (Abstract.)

Brown, L. E. 1956. Movements of some British small mammals. J. Animal Ecol. 25(1):54-71.

Brown, L. G., and L. E. Yeager. 1943. Survey of the Illinois fur resource. Illinois Nat. Hist. Survey Bull. 22(6):435-504 + plate.

Burns, E. 1953. The sex life of wild animals. A North American study. Rinehart and Company, Inc., New York. xiii + 290 pp.

Burt, W. H. 1943. Territoriality and home range concepts as applied to mammals. J. Mammal. 24(3):346-352.

————. 1946. The mammals of Michigan. Univ. Michigan Press, Ann Arbor. xv + 288 pp.

Cahalane, V. H. 1947. Mammals of North America. The Macmillan Company, New York. x + 682 pp.

Campbell, H., and R. E. Tomlinson. 1962. Lens weights in chukar partridges. J. Wildl. Mgmt. 26(4):407-409.

Chandler, A. C. 1952. Two new species of *Oochoristica* from Minnesota skunks. Am. Midland Naturalist 48(1):69-73.

Chapman, F. B. 1946. An interesting feeding habit of skunks. J. Mammal. 27(4):397.

Cheatum, E. L., and A. H. Cook. 1948. On the occurrence of the North American guinea worm in mink, otter, raccoon, and skunk in New York state. Cornell Vet. 38(4):421-423.

Clark, L. G. 1962 (1961). Leptospirosis in Pennsylvania — a progress report. Proc. U. S. Livestock Sanit. Assoc. 65:140-146.

Cochran, W. W., and R. D. Lord, Jr. 1963. A radio-tracking system for wild animals. J. Wildl. Mgmt. 27(1):9-24.

Cole, H. E. 1921. A swimming skunk. Wisconsin Conserv. 3(4):6.

Communicable Disease Center. 1961. Rabies surveillance. Table 1. Reported incidence of rabies in the U. S. 1938-1960. Vet. Public Health Newsletter. Public Health Serv., U. S. Dept. Health, Ed., and Welfare. Sept. 1961. p. 8.

————. 1962. Rabies surveillance. Incidence of rabies in the United States by type of animal and state, 1961. Vet. Public Health Notes. Public Health Serv., U. S. Dept. Health, Ed., and Welfare. July 1962. pp. 4-5.

————. 1963a. Annual rabies surveillance report, 1962. Vet. Public Health Notes. Public Health Serv., U. S. Dept. Health, Ed., and Welfare. April 1963. pp. 3-15.

————. 1963b. Rabies surveillance. South Carolina — 38th state to report bat rabies. Vet. Public Health Notes. Public Health Serv., U. S. Dept. Health, Ed., and Welfare. July 1963. p. 1.

Constantine, D. G. 1962. Rabies transmission by nonbite route. Public Health Rept. 77(4):287-289.

Constantinesco, N., and N. Birzu. 1958. Phénomène d'autostérilisation et guérison dans la rage expérimentale. Ann. Inst. Pasteur (Paris) 94(6):739-747.

Cory, C. B. 1912. The mammals of Illinois and Wisconsin. Field Museum Nat. Hist. Publ. 153, Zool. Ser., Vol. 11. 505 pp.

Coues, E. 1877. Fur-bearing animals: a monograph of North American Mustelidae, in which an account of the wolverene, the martens or sables, the ermine, the mink and various other kinds of weasels, several species of skunks, the badger, the land and sea otters, and numerous exotic allies of these animals, is contributed to the history of North American mammals. Dept. Int., U. S. Geol. of the Territories Misc. Publ. 8. Washington, Government Printing Office. xiv + 348 pp. + Plates 1-20.

Crabb, W. D. 1948. The ecology and management of the prairie spotted skunk in Iowa. Ecol. Monographs 18(2):201-232.

Dahlgren, R. B., C. M. Twedt, and F. R. Henderson. 1964. Lens weights of sharp-tailed grouse. J. Wildl. Mgmt. 28(4):853-854.

Davis, W. B. 1951. Texas skunks. Texas Game & Fish 9(4):18-21, 31.

Dawson, A. B. 1941. The development and morphology of the corpus luteum of the cat. Anat. Record 79(2):155-177.

———, and Betty Ann Kosters. 1944. Preimplantation changes in the uterine musosa (sic) of the cat. Am. J. Anat. 75(1):1-37.

Densmore, Frances. 1923. Mandan and Hidatsa music. Smithsonian Inst., Bur. Am. Ethnol. Bull. 80. xx + 192 pp.

Detlefsen, J. A., and F. M. Holbrook. 1921. Skunk breeding. J. Heredity 12(6):242-254.

Dice, L. R. 1921. Erroneous ideas concerning skunks. J. Mammal. 2(1):38.

———. 1926. Skunk eats kittens. J. Mammal. 7(2):131.

Dikmans, G., and A. Goldberg. 1949. A note on *Arthrocephalus lotoris* (Schwartz, 1925) Chandler, 1942 and other roundworm parasites of the skunk, *Mephitis nigra*. Proc. Helminthol. Soc. Washington 16(1):9-11.

Dixon, J. 1925. Food predilections of predatory and fur-bearing mammals. J. Mammal. 6(1):34-46.

Downie, A. W. 1963. Pathways of virus infection. Pages 101-152. *In* W. Smith (Editor), Mechanisms of virus infection. Academic Press, London and New York. ix + 368 pp.

Durant, A. J., and E. R. Doll. 1939. Pulmonary aspergillosis in a skunk. J. Am. Vet. Med. Assoc. 95(752):645-646.

Edwards, W. R. 1962. Age structure of Ohio cottontail populations from weights of lenses. J. Wildl. Mgmt. 26(2):125-132.

Ellis, M. M., and O. W. Barlow. 1925. Some physiological observations on captive skunks. J. Mammal. 6(1):56-57.

Emmons, C. W., D. A. Rowley, B. J. Olson, C. F. T. Mattern, J. A. Bell, E. Powell, and E. A. Marcey. 1955. Histoplasmosis. Proved occurrence of inapparent infection in dogs, cats and other animals. Am. J. Hyg. 61(1):40-44.

Erickson, A. B. 1946. Incidence of worm parasites in Minnesota Mustelidae and host lists and keys to North American species. Am. Midland Naturalist 36(2):494-509.

Fernald, M. L. 1950. Gray's manual of botany. 8th (Centennial) ed. American Book Company, New York. lxiv + 1632 pp.

Ferris, D. H., L. E. Hanson, A. B. Hoerlein, and P. D. Beamer. 1960. Experimental infection of white-tailed deer with *Leptospira pomona*. Cornell Vet. 50(3):236-250.

———, ———, H. E. Rhoades, and J. O. Alberts. 1961a. Bacteriologic and serologic investigations of brucellosis and leptospirosis in Illinois deer. J. Am. Vet. Med. Assoc. 139(8):892-896.

———, ———, and C. A. Brandly. 1961b. Q fever in Illinois — 1958 to 1960. Prevalence of reactors and infections in livestock. J. Am. Vet. Med. Assoc. 139(10):1111-15.

————, and B. J. Verts. 1964. Leptospiral reactor rates among white-tailed deer and livestock in Carroll County, Illinois. J. Wildl. Mgmt. 28(1): 35-41.

Folk, G. E., Jr. 1963. Hibernation and reproduction of animals. Subsect. A. Hibernation. Pages 703-709. In S. W. Tromp, Medical biometeorology. Weather, climate and the living organism. Elsevier Publishing Company, Amsterdam, London, New York. xxvii + 991 pp.

Fox, H. 1923. Disease in captive wild mammals and birds. Incidence, description, comparison. J. B. Lippincott Company, Philadelphia. vii + 665 pp.

Fox, I. 1940. Fleas of eastern United States. The Iowa State College Press, Ames. vii + 191 pp.

Galloway, I. A., and W. J. Elford. 1936. The size of the virus of rabies ("fixed" strain) by ultrafiltration analysis. J. Hyg. 36(4):532-535.

Galton, Mildred M., G. W. Gorman, and E. B. Shotts, Jr. 1960. A new leptospiral subserotype in the hebdomadis group. Public Health Rept. 75(10):917-921.

Gier, H. T. 1948. Rabies in the wild. J. Wildl. Mgmt. 12(2):142-153.

Goble, F. C. 1942a. *Crenosoma zederi* n. sp. (Nematoda:Metastrongyloidea), a new lungworm from the skunk (*Mephitis nigra*). J. Parasitol. 28(5):381-384.

————. 1942b. *Skrjabingylus chitwoodorum* from the frontal sinuses of *Mephitis nigra* in New York. J. Mammal. 23(1):96-97.

Goldberg, A. 1954. Parasites of skunks in the Beltsville, Maryland, area. Proc. Helminthol. Soc. Washington 21(1):29-34.

Goodpaster, W., and D. F. Hoffmeister. 1950. Bats as prey for mink in Kentucky cave. J. Mammal. 31(4):457.

Gorman, G. W., S. McKeever, and R. D. Grimes. 1962. Leptospirosis in wild mammals from southwestern Georgia. Am. J. Trop. Med. and Hyg. 11(4):518-524.

Goss, L. J. 1948. Species susceptibility to the viruses of Carré and feline enteritis. Am. J. Vet. Research 9(30):65-68.

Gray, M. L. 1964. Infections due to *Listeria monocytogenes* in wildlife. Trans. N. Am. Wildl. and Nat. Resources Conf. 29:202-214.

Grinnell, J., J. S. Dixon, and J. M. Linsdale. 1937. Fur-bearing mammals of California. Their natural history, systematic status, and relations to man. Vol. 1. Univ. California Press, Berkeley. xii + 375 pp.

Hall, E. R. 1955. Handbook of mammals of Kansas. Univ. Kansas Museum Nat. Hist. Misc. Publ. 7. 303 pp.

————, and K. R. Kelson. 1959. The mammals of North America. Ronald Press Company, New York. Vol. 1. xxx + 1-546 + 79 (index) pp. Vol. 2. viii + 547-1083 + 79 (index repeated) pp.

Hamilton, W. J., Jr. 1936. Seasonal food of skunks in New York. J. Mammal. 17(3):240-246.

————. 1937. Winter activity of the skunk. Ecology 18(2):326-327.

————. 1943. The mammals of eastern United States. An account of recent land mammals occurring east of the Mississippi. Handbooks of American

Natural History, Vol. 2. Comstock Publishing Company, Inc., Ithaca, New York. 432 pp.

———. 1963. Reproduction of the striped skunk in New York. J. Mammal. 44(1):123-124.

Hanson, H. C. 1962. The dynamics of condition factors in Canada geese and their relation to seasonal stresses. Arctic Inst. N. Am. Tech. Paper 12. 68 pp.

Hanson, L. E., and J. R. Pickard. 1958. Incidence of *Leptospira pomona* and other leptospiral species serotypes in cattle and swine in Illinois. Illinois Vet. 1(2):41-42.

———, H. C. Ellinghausen, and Rachel Marlowe. 1964. Isolation of *Leptospira grippotyphosa* from a cow following an abortion. (29618) Proc. Soc. Exptl. Biol. and Med. 117(2):495-497.

Hayne, D. W. 1949. Calculation of size of home range. J. Mammal. 30(1): 1-18.

———. 1950. Apparent home range of *Microtus* in relation to distance between traps. J. Mammal. 31(1):26-39.

Helmboldt, C. F., and E. L. Jungherr. 1955. Distemper complex in wild carnivores simulating rabies. Am. J. Vet. Research 16(60):463-469.

Henderson, J., and J. P. Harrington. 1914. Ethnozoology of the Tewa Indians. Smithsonian Inst. Bur. Am. Ethnol. Bull. 56. x + 76 pp.

Hill, W. C. 1939. The nematode *Skrjabingylus chitwoodorum* n. sp. from the skunk. J. Parasitol. 25(6):475-478.

Hobmaier, M. 1941. Description and extramammalian life in *Crenosoma mephitidis* n. sp. (Nematoda) in skunks. J. Parasitol. 27(3):229-232.

Hoffmeister, D. F., and C. O. Mohr. 1957. Fieldbook of Illinois mammals. Illinois Nat. Hist. Survey Div., Manual 4, Urbana. xi + 233 pp.

Howell, A. B. 1943. An apparent mustelid trait. J. Mammal. 24(1):98-99.

Hyatt, H. M. 1935. Folk-lore from Adams County Illinois. Memoirs of the Alma Egan Hyatt Foundation, New York. xvi + 723 pp.

Jackson, H. H. T. 1961. Mammals of Wisconsin. Univ. Wisconsin Press, Madison. xii + 504 pp.

Jaeger, E. C. 1955. A source-book of biological names and terms. 3rd ed. Charles C Thomas–Publisher, Springfield, Illinois. xxxv + 317 pp.

Jellison, W. L. 1947. Siphonaptera: host distribution of the genus *Opisocrostis* Jordan. Trans. Am. Microscop. Soc. 66(1):64-69.

Jennings, W. L., N. J. Schneider, A. L. Lewis, and J. E. Scatterday. 1960. Fox rabies in Florida. J. Wildl. Mgmt. 24(2):171-179.

Johnson, C. E. 1921. The "hand-stand" habit of the spotted skunk. J. Mammal. 2(2):87-89.

Johnson, H. N. 1959. Rabies. Pages 405-431. *In* T. M. Rivers and F. L. Horsfall, Jr. (Editors), Viral and rickettsial infections of man. 3rd ed. J. B. Lippincott Company, Philadelphia and Montreal. xviii + 967 pp.

———. 1960 (1959). The role of the spotted skunk in rabies. Proc. U. S. Livestock Sanit. Assoc. 63:267-274.

Jones, F. H. 1950. Natural history of the striped skunk in northeastern Kansas. M.A. Thesis. Univ. Kansas, Lawrence. 38 pp.

Jones, H. W., Jr. 1939. Winter studies of skunks in Pennsylvania. J. Mammal. 20(2):254-256.

Jones, J. W. 1914. Fur-farming in Canada. 2nd ed. The Mortimer Co., Ltd., Ottawa. viii + 278 pp.

Jones, W. 1911. Notes on the Fox Indians. J. Am. Folk-lore 24(92):209-237.

Jordan, J. S. 1953. Effects of starvation on wild mallards. J. Wildl. Mgmt. 17(3):304-311.

Junod, F. L., and H. Bezdek. 1945. Pleuritis in wild skunk. J. Mammal. 26(3):309-310.

Kalmbach, E. R. 1938. A comparative study of nesting waterfowl on Lower Souris Refuge: 1936-1937. Trans. N. Am. Wildl. Conf. 3:610-623.

Kellogg, V. L., and G. F. Ferris. 1915. The Anoplura and Mallophaga of North American mammals. Leland Stanford Junior Univ. Publ., Univ. Ser., Stanford Univ. Press, Stanford Univ., California. 74 pp.

Kelser, R. A. 1955. Rabies. Pages 250-280. In T. G. Hull, Diseases transmitted from animals to man. 4th ed. Charles C Thomas–Publisher, Springfield, Illinois. xx + 717 pp.

Kimball, J. W. 1948. Pheasant population characteristics and trends in the Dakotas. Trans. N. Am. Wildl. Conf. 13:291-311.

King, Doris C. 1944. Skunk and egg. Readers' Digest 44(266):85.

Kitze, Lois K., with the assistance of Hazel C. Hiemstra and Maria S. Moore. 1957. Q fever in Wisconsin. Serologic evidence of infection in cattle and in human beings and recovery of C. burneti from cattle. Am. J. Hyg. 65(3):239-247.

Kolenosky, G. B., and R. S. Miller. 1962. Growth of the lens of the pronghorn antelope. J. Wildl. Mgmt. 26(1):112-113.

Konradi, D. 1916. Hérédité de la rage. Ann. Inst. Pasteur (Paris) 30(1):33-48.

Koprowski, H. 1952. Latent or dormant viral infections. New York Acad. Sci. Ann. 54(6):963-976.

————. 1954. Mouse inoculation test. Pages 56-58. Part 1, Laboratory diagnosis. Sect. 4. In Laboratory techniques in rabies. World Health Organization Monograph Ser., No. 23. 150 pp.

Kroeber, A. L. 1900. Cheyenne tales. J. Am. Folk-lore 13(50):161-190.

Labisky, R. F. 1959. Night-lighting: a technique for capturing birds and mammals. Illinois Nat. Hist. Survey Biol. Notes 40. 11 pp.

Lane, Kit. 1962. Hey, gals. Skunks, wigs, and kids. Southern Illinoisan, Nov. 29:6.

Lantz, D. E. 1923. Economic value of North American skunks. U. S. Dept. Agr. Farmers' Bull. 587. 24 pp. (Revision.)

Latimer, H. B. 1937. Weights and linear dimensions of the skull and some of the long bones of the skunk (Mephitis mesomelas avia). J. Morphol. 60(2):379-391.

Laun, H. C. 1962. Loud vocal sounds produced by striped skunk. J. Mammal. 43(3):432-433.

Laut, Agnes C. 1921. The fur trade of America. The Macmillan Company, New York. xv + 341 pp.

Layne, J. N. 1958. Records of fleas (Siphonaptera) from Illinois mammals. Chicago Acad. Sci., Nat. Hist. Misc. 162. 7 pp.

Leach, B. J., and C. H. Conaway. 1963. The origin and fate of polyovular follicles in the striped skunk. J. Mammal. 44(1):67-74.

Leigh, W. H. 1940. Preliminary studies on parasites of upland game birds and fur-bearing mammals in Illinois. Illinois Nat. Hist. Survey Bull. 21(5):185-194 + plate.

Leopold, A. S. 1959. Wildlife of Mexico. The game birds and mammals. Univ. California Press, Berkeley and Los Angeles. xiii + 568 pp.

Levine, N. D., Virginia Ivens, T. R. B. Barr, and B. J. Verts. 1962. *Skrjabingylus chitwoodorum* (Nematoda:Metastrongylidae) in skunks in Illinois. Trans. Illinois State Acad. Sci. 55(1):3-5.

————, ————, J. R. Reilly, and J. Simon. 1965. *Filaroides milksi* (Nematoda: Filaroididae) in the lungs of a striped skunk, *Mephitis mephitis*. J. Parasitol. 51(4):628-630.

Liche, H. 1939. Oestrous cycle in the cat. Nature 143(3630):900.

Linduska, J. P. 1947. Longevity of some Michigan farm game mammals. J. Mammal. 28(2):126-129.

Linhart, S. B. 1960. Rabies in wildlife and control methods in New York State. New York Fish and Game J. 7(1):1-13.

Llewellyn, L. M. 1953. Growth rate of the raccoon fetus. J. Wildl. Mgmt. 17(3):320-321.

————, and F. M. Uhler. 1952. The foods of fur animals of the Patuxent Research Refuge, Maryland. Am. Midland Naturalist 48(1):193-203.

Lord, R. D., Jr. 1959. The lens as an indicator of age in cottontail rabbits. J. Wildl. Mgmt. 23(3):358-360.

————. 1961. The lens as an indicator of age in the gray fox. J. Mammal. 42(1):109-111.

————. 1962. Aging deer and determination of their nutritional status by the lens technique. Proc. Natl. White-tailed Deer Disease Symposium 1: 89-94. Univ. Georgia Center for Continuing Ed., Athens. February 13-15, 1962.

Luoto, L. 1953. A capillary agglutination test for bovine Q fever. J. Immunol. 71(4):226-231.

————. 1960. Report on the nationwide occurrence of Q fever infections in cattle. Public Health Rept. 75(2):135-140.

McKeever, S., G. W. Gorman, J. F. Chapman, M. M. Galton, and D. K. Powers. 1958a. Incidence of leptospirosis in wild mammals from southwestern Georgia, with a report of new hosts for six serotypes of leptospires. Am. J. Trop. Med. Hyg. 7(6):646-655.

————, W. Kaplan, and L. Ajello. 1958b. Ringworm fungi of large wild mammals in southwestern Georgia and northwestern Florida. Am. J. Vet. Research 19(73):973-975.

————, J. H. Schubert, M. D. Moody, G. W. Gorman, and J. F. Chapman. 1958c. Natural occurrence of tularemia in marsupials, carnivores, lagomorphs, and large rodents in southwestern Georgia and northwestern Florida. J. Infect. Diseases 103(2):120-126.

McKiel, J. A., J. G. Cousineau, and R. R. Hall. 1961. Leptospirosis in wild animals in eastern Canada with particular attention to the disease in rats. Canadian J. Comp. Med. Vet. Sci. 25(1):15-18.

MacLulich, D. A. 1936. Running speeds of skunk and European hare. Canadian Field-Naturalist 50(5):92.

Martin, J. H., and W. H. Leonard. 1949. Principles of field crop production. The Macmillan Company, New York. ix + 1176 pp.

Martin, R. L. 1959. A history of chiropteran rabies with special reference to occurrence and importance in the United States. Wildl. Disease 3:card 1 (of 1):1-75.

Matsumoto, S. 1962. Electron microscopy of nerve cells infected with street rabies virus. Virology 17(1):198-202.

Mead, R. A. 1963. Some aspects of parasitism in skunks of the Sacramento Valley of California. Am. Midland Naturalist 70(1):164-167.

Menges, R. W., R. T. Habermann, and H. J. Stains. 1955. A distemper-like disease in raccoons and isolation of *Histoplasma capsulatum* and *Haplosporangium parvum*. Trans. Kansas Acad. Sci. 58(1):58-67.

————, and Lucille K. Georg. 1957. Survey of animal ringworm in the United States. Public Health Rept. 72(6):503-509.

Merchant, I. A., and R. A. Packer. 1961. Veterinary bacteriology and virology. 6th ed. Iowa State Univ. Press, Ames. viii + 899 pp.

Metcalf, C. L., and W. P. Flint. 1951. Destructive and useful insects. Their habits and control. 3rd ed. (Revised by R. L. Metcalf.) McGraw-Hill Book Company, Inc., New York. xiv + 1071 pp.

Miller, G. S., Jr., and R. Kellogg. 1955. List of North American recent mammals. U. S. Natl. Museum Bull. 205. xii + 954 pp.

Mohr, C. O. 1943. Illinois furbearer distribution and income. Illinois Nat. Hist. Survey Bull. 22(7):505-537 + plates.

Mooney, J. 1900. Myths of the Cherokee. Bur. Am. Ethnol. 19th Annual Rept. (1897-98). Part 1. Government Printing Office, Washington, D. C. xcii + 576 pp.

Morlan, H. B., E. L. Hill, and J. H. Schubert. 1950. Serological survey for murine typhus infection in southwest Georgia animals. Public Health Rept. 65(2):57-63.

Mueller, J. F. 1927. Two new species of the cestode genus *Mesocestoides*. Am. Microscop. Soc. Trans. 46(4):294.

Murie, O. J. 1954. A field guide to animal tracks. The Peterson Field Guide Series 9. Houghton Mifflin Company, Boston; The Riverside Press, Cambridge. xxii + 374 pp.

Mykytowycz, R. 1961. Social behaviour of an experimental colony of wild rabbits, *Oryctolagus cuniculus* (L.). IV. Conclusion: outbreak of myxomatosis, third breeding season, and starvation. C. S. I. R. O. Wildl. Research 6(2):142-155.

Nelson, E. W. 1930. Wild animals of North America. Intimate studies of big and little creatures of the mammal kingdom. The Natl. Geog. Soc., Washington, D.C. viii + 254 pp.

Norman, Lois, M. M. Brooke, D. S. Allain, and G. W. Gorman. 1959. Morphology and virulence of *Trypanosoma cruzi*–like hemoflagellates isolated from wild mammals in Georgia and Florida. J. Parasitol. 45(4):457-463.

Nuttall, Zelia. 1895. A note on ancient Mexican folk-lore. J. Am. Folk-lore 8(29):117-129.

Osebold, J. W., G. Shultz, and E. W. Jameson, Jr. 1957. An epizootiological study of listeriosis. J. Am. Vet. Med. Assoc. 130(11):471-475.

Parker, R. L. 1962 (1961). Rabies in skunks in the North-Central States. Proc. U. S. Livestock Sanit. Assoc. 65:273-280.

———, J. W. Kelly, E. L. Cheatum, and D. J. Dean. 1957. Fox population densities in relation to rabies. New York Fish and Game J. 4(2):219-228.

Patera, E. 1956. Azione del cortisone nell'infezione sperimentale del coniglio con virus rabbico fisso. Atti della Società delle Scienze Veterinarie 10:667-669. (In Italian; English summary.)

Pawan, J. L. 1936. Rabies in the vampire bat of Trinidad, with special reference to the clinical course and the latency of infection. Ann. Trop. Med. and Parasitol. 30(4):401-422.

Payne, R. B. 1961. Growth rates of the lens of the eye of house sparrows. Condor 63(4):338-340.

Pearson, E. W., and T. R. B. Barr. 1962. Absence of rabies in some bats and shrews from southern Illinois. Trans. Illinois State Acad. Sci. 55(1):35-37.

Phares, R. 1956. Animals: fact and fancy. Florida Wildl. 9(8):22-23.

Philological Society, The. 1933 (Reprinted 1961). The Oxford English dictionary. Vol. 9. S-Soldo. (Si.-St.). The Clarendon Press, Oxford. 1186 pp.

Quick, H. F. 1963. Animal population analysis. Pages 190-228. In H. S. Mosby (Editor), Wildlife investigational techniques. 2nd ed. Printed for the Wildlife Society by Edwards Brothers, Inc., Ann Arbor, Michigan. xxiv + 419 pp.

Rainey, D. G. 1956. Eastern woodrat, Neotoma floridana: life history and ecology. Univ. Kansas Publ., Museum Nat. Hist. 8(10):535-646.

Remlinger, P. 1919. Contribution a l'étude de l'hérédité de la rage. Ann. Inst. Pasteur (Paris) 33(5):375-388.

Rhodes, A. J., and C. E. van Rooyen. 1962. Textbook of virology for students and practitioners of medicine. 4th ed. The Williams & Wilkins Company, Baltimore. xvi + 600 pp.

Richards, S. 1957. Rabies in North Dakota wildlife. North Dakota Outdoors 20(5):4-5, 16.

Roseberry, J. L., and B. J. Verts. 1963. Relationships between lens-weight, sex, and age in bobwhites. Trans. Illinois State Acad. Sci. 56(4):208-212.

Roth, E. E. 1961. Leptospirosis in striped skunks. M.Sc. Thesis. Texas A. & M. College, College Station. 58 pp.

———, W. V. Adams, and Donna Linder. 1961. Isolation of Leptospira canicola from skunks in Louisiana. Public Health Rept. 76(4):335-340.

———, ———, G. E. Sanford, Jr., Betty Greer, Kay Newman, Mary Moore, Patricia Mayeux, and Donna Linder. 1963a. The bacteriologic and serologic incidence of leptospirosis among striped skunks in Louisiana. Zoonoses Research 2(1):13-39.

———, ———, ———, Mary Moore, Kay Newman, and Betty Greer. 1963b. Leptospiruria in striped skunks. Public Health Rept. 78(11):994-1000.

Sagard, Theodat, F. G. 1636. Histoire du Canada. C. Sonnius, Paris. 1016 pp.

Sanderson, G. C. 1961a. Techniques for determining age of raccoons. Illinois Nat. Hist. Survey Biol. Notes 45. 16 pp.

————. 1961*b*. The reproductive cycle and related phenomena in the raccoon. Ph.D. Thesis. Univ. Illinois, Urbana. 156 pp.

————. 1961*c*. The lens as an indicator of age in the raccoon. Am. Midland Naturalist 65(2):481-485.

Scatterday, J. E., N. J. Schneider, W. L. Jennings, and A. L. Lewis. 1960. Sporadic animal rabies in Florida. Public Health Rept. 75(10):945-953.

Schmidt, K. P. 1936. Dehairing of caterpillars by skunks. J. Mammal. 17(3):287.

Schoening, H. W. 1956. Rabies. Pages 195-202. *In* The yearbook of agriculture 1956: animal diseases. U. S. Govt. Printing Office, Washington, D. C. xiv + 591 pp.

Schwartz, C. W., and Elizabeth R. Schwartz. 1959. The wild mammals of Missouri. Univ. Missouri Press and Missouri Conserv. Comm. viii + [8] + 341 pp.

Scott, T. G. 1943. Some food coactions of the northern plains red fox. Ecol. Monographs 13(4):427-479.

————, and L. F. Selko. 1939. A census of red foxes and striped skunks in Clay and Boone counties, Iowa. J. Wildl. Mgmt. 3(2):92-98.

————, and E. Snead. 1942. Warbles in *Peromyscus leucopus noveboracensis*. J. Mammal. 23(1):94-95.

————, Y. L. Willis, and J. A. Ellis. 1959. Some effects of a field application of dieldrin on wildlife. J. Wildl. Mgmt. 23(4):409-427.

Self, J. T., and T. J. McKnight. 1950. Platyhelminths from fur bearers in the Wichita Mountains Wildlife Refuge, with especial reference to *Oochoristica* spp. Am. Midland Naturalist 43(1):58-61.

Selko, L. F. 1937. Food habits of Iowa skunks in the fall of 1936. J. Wildl. Mgmt. 1(3-4):70-76.

————. 1938*a*. Hibernation of the striped skunk in Iowa. J. Mammal. 19(3):320-324.

————. 1938*b*. Notes on the den ecology of the striped skunk in Iowa. Am. Midland Naturalist 20(2):455-463.

Seton, E. T. 1909. Life-histories of northern animals. An account of the mammals of Manitoba. Vol. 1. Grass-eaters. xxx + 3-673 pp. Vol. 2. Flesh-eaters. xii + 667-1267 pp. Charles Scribner's Sons, New York City.

————. 1920. Acrobatic skunks. J. Mammal. 1(3):140.

————. 1926. Lives of game animals. An account of those land animals in America, north of the Mexican border, which are considered "game," either because they have held the attention of sportsmen, or received the protection of law. Vol. 2. Doubleday, Page and Company, Garden City, New York. xviii + 746 pp.

Shadle, A. R. 1953. Captive striped skunk produces two litters. J. Wildl. Mgmt. 17(3):388-389.

————. 1956. Parturition in a skunk, *Mephitis mephitis hudsonica*. J. Mammal. 37(1):112-113.

Shepard, C. C. 1947. An outbreak of Q fever in a Chicago packing house. Am. J. Hyg. 46(2):185-192.

Sikes, R. K. 1962. Pathogenesis of rabies in wildlife. I. Comparative effect of varying doses of rabies virus inoculated into foxes and skunks. Am. J. Vet. Research 23(96):1041-47.

Sims, Ruth A., Rae Allen, and S. E. Sulkin. 1963. Studies on the pathogenesis of rabies in insectivorous bats. III. Influence of the gravid state. J. Infect. Diseases 112(1) :17-27.

Skinker, Mary Scott. 1935. A new species of *Oochoristica* from a skunk. J. Washington Acad. Sci. 25(2) :59-65.

Smith, K. M. 1950. An introduction to the study of viruses. Pitman Publishing Corporation, New York. ix + 106 pp.

Smith, P. W. 1961. The amphibians and reptiles of Illinois. Illinois Nat. Hist. Survey Bull. 28(1) :1-298.

Smith, W. 1963. Mechanisms of virus infection. General considerations. Pages 1-34. *In* W. Smith (Editor), Mechanisms of virus infection. Academic Press, London and New York. ix + 368 pp.

Smith, W. P. 1931. Calendar of disappearance and emergence of some hibernating mammals at Wells River, Vermont. J. Mammal. 12(1) :78-79.

Smythe, R. H. 1961. Animal vision. What animals see. Charles C Thomas–Publisher, Springfield, Illinois. 250 pp.

Snyder, R. L., and J. J. Christian. 1960. Reproductive cycle and litter size of the woodchuck. Ecology 41(4) :647-656.

Soave, O. A. 1966. Transmission of rabies to mice by ingestion of infected tissue. Am. J. Vet. Research 27(116) :44-46.

————, H. N. Johnson, and K. Nakamura. 1961. Reactivation of rabies virus infection with adrenocorticotropic hormones. Science 133(3461) :1360-61.

Sohval, A. R. 1958. The anatomy and endocrine physiology of the male reproductive system. Pages 243-312. *In* J. T. Velardo (Editor), The endocrinology of reproduction. Oxford University Press, New York. viii + 340 pp.

Sperry, C. C. 1933. Opossum and skunk eat bats. J. Mammal. 14(2) :152-153.

Spindler, L. A., and D. O. Permenter. 1951. Natural infections of *Trichinella spiralis* in skunks. J. Parasitol. 37(5, sect. 2, suppl.) :19-20. (Abstract.)

Stains, H. J., and D. Stuckey. 1960. Brachial-antebrachial stripes on a striped skunk. J. Mammal. 41(1) :139.

Stannard, L. J., Jr., and L. R. Pietsch. 1958. Ectoparasites of the cottontail rabbit in Lee County, northern Illinois. Illinois Nat. Hist. Survey Biol. Notes 38. 18 pp.

Steel, R. G. D., and J. H. Torrie. 1960. Principles and procedures of statistics with special reference to the biological sciences. McGraw-Hill Book Company, Inc., New York. xvi + 481 pp.

Steele, J. H. 1960. Epidemiology of leptospirosis in the United States and Canada. J. Am. Vet. Med. Assoc. 136(6) :247-252.

Stegeman, L. C. 1939. Some parasites and pathological conditions of the skunk (*Mephitis mephitis nigra*) in central New York. J. Mammal. 20(4) : 493-496.

Stiles, C. W., and Clara Edith Baker. 1935. Key-catalogue of parasites reported for Carnivora (cats, dogs, bears, etc.) with their possible public health importance. Natl. Inst. Health Bull. 163:913-1223.

Stoddard, H. L., and E. V. Komarek. 1941. Predator control in southeastern quail management. Trans. N. Am. Wildl. Conf. 6:288-293.

Storer, T. I., and G. H. Vansell. 1935. Bee-eating proclivities of the striped skunk. J. Mammal. 16(2):118-121.

Storm, G. L., and B. J. Verts. 1966. Movements of a striped skunk infected with rabies. J. Mammal. 47(4):705-708.

Stumpf, W. A., and C. O. Mohr. 1962. Linearity of home ranges of California mice and other animals. J. Wildl. Mgmt. 26(2):149-154.

Sulkin, S. E. 1962. Bat rabies: experimental demonstration of the "reservoiring mechanism." Am. J. Public Health 52(3):489-498.

————, P. H. Krutzsch, C. Wallis, and Rae Allen. 1957. Role of brown fat in pathogenesis of rabies in insectivorous bats (*Tadarida b. mexicana*). Proc. Soc. Exptl. Biol. Med. 96:461-464.

————, Rae Allen, Ruth Sims, P. H. Krutzsch, and Chansoo Kim. 1960. Studies on the pathogenesis of rabies in insectivorous bats. II. Influence of environmental temperature. J. Exptl. Med. 112(4):595-617.

Swanson, G., and A. B. Erickson. 1946. *Alaria taxideae* n. sp. from the badger and other mustelids. J. Parasitol. 32(1):17-19.

Terres, J. K. 1940. Notes on the winter activity of a captive skunk. J. Mammal. 21(2):216-217.

Thiery, G. 1959. La rage en Afrique occidentale. Ses particularités. Sa contagiosité. Rev. d' Elévage et de Méd. Vét. des Pays Trop. 12(1):27-42.

Tierkel, E. S. 1958. Part IV. Recent developments in the epidemiology of rabies. New York Acad. Sci. Ann. 70(3):445-448.

————. 1959. Rabies. Pages 183-226. *In* C. A. Brandly and E. L. Jungherr (Editors), Advances in veterinary science. Vol. 5. Academic Press, Inc., Publishers, New York and London. xi + 450 pp.

Tiner, J. D. 1946. Some helminth parasites of skunks in Texas. J. Mammal. 27(1):82-83.

Van Cleave, H. J. 1953. Acanthocephala of North American mammals. Illinois Biol. Monographs 23(1-2):x + 1-179.

Venters, H. D., W. R. Hoffert, J. E. Scatterday, and A. V. Hardy. 1954. Rabies in bats in Florida. Am. J. Public Health 44(2):182-185.

Verts, B. J. 1960. A device for anesthetizing skunks. J. Wildl. Mgmt. 24(3):335-336.

————. 1961a. A convenient method of carrying and dispensing baits. J. Mammal. 42(2):283.

————. 1961b. Observations on the fleas (Siphonaptera) of some small mammals in northwestern Illinois. Am. Midland Naturalist 66(2):471-476.

————. 1963a. Equipment and techniques for radio-tracking striped skunks. J. Wildl. Mgmt. 27(3):325-339.

————. 1963b. Movements and populations of opossums in a cultivated area. J. Wildl. Mgmt. 27(1):127-129.

————, and T. R. B. Barr. 1960. Apparent absence of rabies in Illinois shrews. J. Wildl. Mgmt. 24(4):438.

————, and ————. 1961. An effort to identify rabies in bats from northwestern Illinois. Cornell Vet. 51(3):384-388.

————, and G. L. Storm. 1966. A local study of prevalence of rabies among foxes and striped skunks. J. Wildl. Mgmt. 30(2):419-421.

Viazhevich, V. K. 1957. A case of birth of a healthy baby to a mother during the incubation period of rabies. J. Microbiol., Epidemiol., and Immunobiol. 28(7/8):1022-23. Translated by J. Saunders from Zh. Mikrobiol., Epidemiol., Immunobiol. 7:105-106, 1957.

Walker, A. 1930. The "hand-stand" and some other habits of the Oregon spotted skunk. J. Mammal. 11(2):227-229.

Walker, E. P., Florence Warnick, K. I. Lange, H. E. Uible, Sybil E. Hamlet, Mary A. Davis, and Patricia F. Wright. 1964. Mammals of the world. Vols. 1 and 2. The Johns Hopkins Press, Baltimore. xlviii + viii + 1500 pp.

Wallace, F. G. 1935. A morphological and biological study of the trematode, *Sellacotyle mustelae* n. g., n. sp. J. Parasitol. 21(3):143-164. Plates 1 and 2.

————. 1941. *Crenosoma microbursa* n. sp. from the skunk. Proc. Helminthol. Soc. Washington 8(2):58-60.

Webster, Gloria A., and R. W. Wolfgang. 1956. *Alaria canadensis* sp. nov. and *Euryhelmis pyriformis* sp. nov. from the skunk *Mephitis mephitis* in Quebec. Canadian J. Zool. 34(6):595-601.

Wight, H. M. 1931. Reproduction in the eastern skunk (*Mephitis mephitis nigra*). J. Mammal. 12(1):42-47.

Wilber, C. G., and G. H. Weidenbacher. 1961. Swimming capacity of some wild mammals. J. Mammal. 42(3):428-429.

Wood, J. E. 1954. Investigation of fox populations and sylvatic rabies in the Southeast. Trans. N. Am. Wildl. Conf. 19:131-140.

Wyman, L. C. 1952. A prehistoric naturalist. Plateau 24(4):2-3. Museum N. Arizona.

Young, S. P. 1958. The bobcat of North America. Its history, life habits, economic status and control, with list of currently recognized subspecies. The Stackpole Company, Harrisburg, Pennsylvania, and the Wildlife Management Institute, Washington, D. C. [xiv] + 193 pp.

————, and H. H. T. Jackson. 1951. The clever coyote. The Stackpole Company, Harrisburg, Pennsylvania, and the Wildlife Management Institute, Washington, D. C. xv + 411 pp.

APPENDIX

Table A. *Lists of common and scientific names* of vertebrate animals referred to in this study.*

Scientific Name	Common Name
AMPHIBIA	
Bufo americanus	American Toad
AVES	
Branta canadensis	Canada Goose
Anas platyrhynchos	Mallard
Aquila chrysaëtos	Golden Eagle
Haliaeetus leucocephalus	Bald Eagle
Colinus virginianus	Bob-white
Phasianus colchicus	Ring-necked Pheasant
Zenaidura macroura	Mourning Dove
Bubo virginianus	Great Horned Owl
Sturnella magna	Eastern Meadowlark
Pipilo erythrophthalmus	Eastern Towhee
Corvus brachyrhynchos	Crow
Cyanocitta cristata	Blue Jay
Agelaius phoeniceus	Red-wing
Gallus gallus	Domestic Chicken
MAMMALIA	
Didelphis marsupialis	Opossum
Scalopus aquaticus	Eastern Mole
Sorex cinereus	Masked Shrew
Blarina brevicauda	Short-tailed Shrew

* In determining scientific nomenclature, reference was made to Hall and Kelson (1959), Miller and Kellogg (1955), Walker *et al.* (1964), Smith (1961), and American Ornithologists' Union (1957).

Table A (Continued)

Scientific Name	Common Name
Tadarida braziliensis	Free-tailed Bat
Desmodus rotundus	Vampire Bat
Procyon lotor	Raccoon
Bassariscus astutus	Ringtail Cat
Mustela frenata	Long-tailed Weasel
Mustela rixosa	Least Weasel
Mustela vison	Mink
Mustela putoris	Ferret
Lutra canadensis	River Otter
Taxidea taxis	Badger
Mephitis mephitis	Striped Skunk
Spilogale putoris	Spotted Skunk
Canis familiaris	Domestic Dog
Canis latrans	Coyote
Vulpes fulva	Red Fox
Urocyon cinereoargenteus	Gray Fox
Alopex lagopus	Arctic Fox
Felis concolor	Mountain Lion
Felis domestica	Domestic Cat
Sciurus carolinensis	Eastern Gray Squirrel
Sciurus niger	Eastern Fox Squirrel
Glaucomys volans	Southern Flying Squirrel
Citellus tridecemlineatus	Thirteen-lined Ground Squirrel
Citellus franklini	Franklin's Ground Squirrel
Marmota monax	Woodchuck
Peromyscus leucopus	White-footed Mouse
Peromyscus maniculatus	Deer Mouse
Neotoma floridana	Eastern Woodrat
Pitymys pinetorum	Pine Vole
Synaptomys cooperi	Southern Bog Lemming
Microtus pennsylvanicus	Meadow Vole
Microtus ochrogaster	Prairie Vole
Ondatra zibethica	Muskrat
Mus musculus	House Mouse
Cavia porcellus	Guinea Pig
Sylvilagus floridanus	Eastern Cottontail Rabbit
Oryctolagus cuniculus	European Rabbit
Sus scrofa	Domestic Pig
Odocoileus virginianus	White-tailed Deer
Homo sapiens	Man (Human)

Table B. *Species occupying 46 ground dens on the Shannon Study Area during August, September, and October, 1960, and at about 2-month intervals during 1961.*

Den Number	Species Occupying Den, 1960	Species Occupying Den on:			
		April 21, 1961	June 27, 1961	August 31, 1961	October 30, 1961
2-1	Badgers	Ground Squirrels	None	None	None
2-2	Badgers	Closed	–	–	–
2-3	None	None	None	Closed	–
2-4	Skunks	Ground Squirrels	None	None	None
2-5	Raccoons	None	Badgers	Badgers	Badgers
2-6	None	Closed	–	–	–
2-7	None	Closed	–	–	–
6-1	None	Closed	–	–	–
6-2	None	None	Closed	–	–
6-3	Skunks	Closed	–	–	–
7-1	None	Skunks	None	Ground Squirrels	Skunks
11-1	None	Closed	–	–	–
12-1	Skunks	Closed	–	–	–
12-2	Raccoons	Skunks	None	Badgers	None
12-3	None	Closed	–	–	–
12-4	None	Closed	–	–	–
12-5	Skunks	None	Badgers	Badgers	Badgers
12-6*	Raccoons	Closed	Raccoons	Raccoons	Raccoons
12-7	Skunks	Closed	–	–	–
12-8	Raccoons	Closed	–	–	–
12-9	Raccoons	None	Closed	Badgers†	Skunks
12-10	Skunks	Closed	–	–	–
12-11	None	None	None	None	Closed
12-13	Badgers	Closed	–	–	–
12-14	None	Rabbits	Closed	–	–
12-15	None	Closed	–	–	–
12-16	Rabbits	Weasels	Rabbits	Rabbits	Closed
12-17	None	Closed	–	–	–
12-18	None	Closed	–	Badgers†	None
12-19	None	Closed	–	–	–
12-20	None	Skunks	Closed	–	–
12-21	None	Closed	–	Skunks†	Skunks

* Den occupied by skunks during winter 1960–61.
† Den reopened since last examination.

Table B (Continued)

Den Number	Species Occupying Den, 1960	Species Occupying Den on:			
		April 21, 1961	June 27, 1961	August 31, 1961	October 30, 1961
12-22	Red Foxes	Closed	–	–	–
12-23	None	Closed	–	–	–
12-24	None	Closed	–	–	–
12-25	None	Closed	–	–	–
1-1	None	Red Foxes	Closed	–	–
1-2	Raccoons	Closed	–	–	–
1-3	None	Closed	–	–	–
1-4	Raccoons	Closed	–	–	–
1-5	Skunks	Closed	–	–	–
1-6	None	Ground Squirrels	None	Ground Squirrels	None
1-7	None	None	None	Ground Squirrels	Ground Squirrels
1-8	Skunks	Closed	–	–	–
1-9	Badgers	Closed	–	–	–
1-10	Badgers	Closed	–	–	–

Table C. The frequency of occurrence and percent frequency of occurrence of food items of striped skunks, determined by analysis of 20 fecal passages and of contents of stomachs and intestines from 149 specimens, northwestern Illinois, January 6, 1960–August 24, 1962. Numerals in parentheses indicate numbers of analyses.

Food Item	Winter (17)		Spring (67)		Summer (49)		Autumn (36)		Totals (169)	
	No.	%	No.	%	No.	%	No.	%	No.	%
INVERTEBRATA	16	94.1	57	85.1	42	85.7	33	91.7	148	87.6
Annelida	–	–	2	3.0	–	–	1	2.8	3	1.8
Oligochaeta	–	–	2	3.0	–	–	1	2.8	3	1.8
Lumbricus sp.	–	–	2	3.0	–	–	1	2.8	3	1.8
Arthropoda	16	94.1	57	85.1	42	85.7	33	91.7	148	87.6
Arachnida	–	–	7	10.4	2	4.0	1	2.8	10	5.9
Spider Egg Cases	–	–	–	–	1	2.0	–	–	1	0.6
Diplopoda	–	–	1	1.5	–	–	2	5.6	3	1.8
Isopoda	–	–	1	1.5	–	–	–	–	1	0.6
Insecta	16	94.1	57	85.1	42	85.7	33	91.7	148	87.6
ADULT FORMS:										
Thysanoptera	–	–	1	1.5	–	–	–	–	1	0.6
Coleoptera	6	35.3	48	71.6	42	85.7	29	80.6	125	74.0
Carabidae	3	17.6	38	56.7	39	79.6	29	80.6	109	64.5
Agonoderus sp.	–	–	1	1.5	–	–	–	–	1	0.6
Species Unknown	3	17.6	37	55.2	39	79.6	29	80.6	108	63.9
Meloidae	–	–	–	–	1	2.0	–	–	1	0.6
Epicauta vittata	–	–	–	–	1	2.0	–	–	1	0.6
Staphylinidae	–	–	–	–	–	–	1	2.8	1	0.6
Cicindelidae	–	–	–	–	2	4.1	–	–	2	1.2
Cicindela punctulata	–	–	–	–	2	4.1	–	–	2	1.2
Curculionidae	2	11.8	7	10.4	6	12.2	1	2.8	16	9.5
Sitona hispidula	–	–	1	1.5	2	4.1	1	2.8	4	2.4

Table C (Continued)

Food Item	Winter (17)		Spring (67)		Summer (49)		Autumn (36)		Totals (169)	
	No.	%	No.	%	No.	%	No.	%	No.	%
Sitona cylindricollis	—	—	1	1.5	—	—	—	—	1	0.6
Hypera punctata	—	—	1	1.5	2	4.1	—	—	3	1.8
Hypera nigrirostris	2	11.8	2	3.0	—	—	—	—	4	2.4
Sphenophorus sp.	—	—	1	1.5	—	—	—	—	1	0.6
Species Unknown	—	—	2	3.0	2	4.1	—	—	4	2.4
Nitidulidae	—	—	2	3.0	2	4.1	1	2.8	5	3.0
Glischrochilus quadrisignatus	—	—	2	3.0	2	4.1	1	2.8	5	3.0
Coccinellidae	—	—	1	1.5	1	2.0	—	—	2	1.2
Coccinella sp.	—	—	1	1.5	—	—	—	—	1	0.6
Species Unknown	—	—	—	—	1	2.0	—	—	1	0.6
Scarabaeidae	1	5.9	29	43.3	8	16.3	2	5.6	40	23.7
Phyllophaga futilis	—	—	8	11.9	—	—	—	—	8	4.7
Phyllophaga fusca	—	—	1	1.5	—	—	—	—	1	0.6
Phyllophaga implicita	—	—	3	4.5	—	—	—	—	3	1.8
Phyllophaga rugosa	—	—	1	1.5	—	—	—	—	1	0.6
Phyllophaga sp.	—	—	9	13.4	1	2.0	—	—	10	5.9
Copris sp.	—	—	8	11.9	—	—	—	—	8	4.7
Aphodius sp.	1	5.9	3	4.5	1	2.0	—	—	5	3.0
Ataenius sp.	—	—	2	3.0	1	2.0	—	—	3	1.8
Bolbocerosoma sp.	—	—	2	3.0	5	10.2	2	5.6	9	5.3
Bothinus sp.	—	—	1	1.5	—	—	—	—	1	0.6
Geotrupes sp.	—	—	1	1.5	—	—	—	—	1	0.6
Silphidae	—	—	1	1.5	1	2.0	—	—	2	1.2
Necrophorus sp.	—	—	1	1.5	1	2.0	—	—	2	1.2
Elateridae	—	—	2	3.0	—	—	—	—	2	1.2

Melanotus sp.	—	—	2	3.0	—	—	—	—	2	1.2
Chrysomelidae	—	—	2	3.0	2	4.1	—	—	4	2.4
Mantura sp.	—	—	1	1.5	—	—	—	—	1	0.6
Altica sp.	—	—	1	1.5	—	—	—	—	1	0.6
Diabrotica longicornis	—	—	—	—	1	2.0	—	—	1	0.6
Diabrotica sp.	—	—	—	—	1	2.0	—	—	1	0.6
Anthribidae	—	—	1	1.5	—	—	—	—	1	0.6
Cryptophagidae	1	5.9	—	—	—	—	—	—	1	0.6
Cucujidae	1	5.9	—	—	—	—	—	—	1	0.6
Telephanus velox	1	5.9	—	—	—	—	—	—	1	0.6
Histeridae	—	—	1	1.5	—	—	—	—	1	0.6
Unknown Family	—	—	—	—	1	2.0	—	—	1	0.6
Orthoptera	10	58.8	4	6.0	27	55.1	31	86.1	72	42.6
Gryllidae	1	5.9	1	1.5	5	10.2	15	41.7	22	13.0
Locustidae	9	52.9	4	6.0	24	49.0	29	80.6	66	39.1
Tettigoniidae	—	—	—	—	1	2.0	2	5.6	3	1.8
Hymenoptera	—	—	11	16.4	16	32.7	—	—	27	16.0
Formicidae	—	—	6	8.9	5	10.2	—	—	11	6.5
Tapinoma sessile	—	—	1	1.5	—	—	—	—	1	0.6
Species Unknown	—	—	5	7.5	5	10.2	—	—	10	5.9
Apidae	—	—	4	6.0	12	24.5	—	—	16	9.5
Family Unknown	—	—	1	1.5	—	—	—	—	1	0.6
Hemiptera	7	41.2	4	6.0	1	2.0	3	8.3	15	8.9
Heteroptera	7	41.2	3	4.5	1	2.0	2	5.6	13	7.7
Nabidae	1	5.9	—	—	—	—	—	—	1	0.6
Nabis sp.	1	5.9	—	—	—	—	—	—	1	0.6
Pentatomidae	6	35.3	3	4.5	—	—	2	5.6	11	6.5
Chlorochroa persimilis	1	5.9	—	—	—	—	—	—	1	0.6
Euschistus sp.	1	5.9	1	1.5	—	—	—	—	2	1.2

Table C (Continued)

Food Item	Winter (17)		Spring (67)		Summer (49)		Autumn (36)		Totals (169)	
	No.	%	No.	%	No.	%	No.	%	No.	%
Species Unknown	4	23.5	2	3.0	–	–	2	5.6	8	4.7
Coreidae	–	–	–	–	1	2.0	–	–	1	0.6
Family Unknown	1	5.9	–	–	1	2.0	–	–	2	1.2
Homoptera	–	–	1	1.5	–	–	–	–	1	0.6
Membracidae	–	–	1	1.5	–	–	–	–	1	0.6
IMMATURE FORMS (LARVAE AND PUPAE):										
Coleoptera	–	–	5	7.5	4	8.2	–	–	9	5.3
Carabidae	–	–	–	–	1	2.0	–	–	1	0.6
Mordellidae	–	–	1	1.5	–	–	–	–	1	0.6
Scarabaeidae	–	–	1	1.5	3	6.1	–	–	4	2.4
Phyllophaga sp.	–	–	–	–	3	6.1	–	–	3	1.8
Species Unknown	–	–	1	1.5	–	–	–	–	1	0.6
Elateridae	–	–	3	4.5	–	–	–	–	3	1.8
Family Unknown	–	–	1	1.5	1	2.0	–	–	2	1.2
Lepidoptera	4	23.5	25	37.3	15	30.6	9	25.0	53	31.4
Arctiidae	2	11.8	3	4.5	5	10.2	5	13.9	15	8.9
Hesperiidae	1	5.9	–	–	–	–	–	–	1	0.6
Noctuidae	–	–	15	22.4	4	8.2	2	5.6	21	12.4
Acronycta sp.	–	–	–	–	–	–	1	2.8	1	0.6
Pseudaletia unipuncta	–	–	1	1.5	–	–	–	–	1	0.6
Species Unknown	–	–	14	20.9	4	8.2	1	2.8	19	11.2
Tortricidae	–	–	1	1.5	–	–	–	–	1	0.6
Family Unknown (Larvae)	1	5.9	7	10.7	3	6.1	2	5.6	13	7.7
Family Unknown (Pupae)	1	5.9	–	–	3	6.1	–	–	4	2.4

	n	%	n	%	n	%	n	%	n	%
Diptera	—	—	9	13.4	5	10.2	5	13.9	19	11.2
Anthomyiidae	—	—	1	1.5	1	2.0	—	—	2	1.2
Sarcophagidae	—	—	1	1.5	—	—	—	—	1	0.6
Unknown Muscoid Larvae	—	—	6	8.9	5	10.2	5	13.9	16	9.5
Family Unknown (Pupae)	—	—	2	2.9	—	—	—	—	2	1.2
VERTEBRATA	11	64.7	50	74.6	34	69.4	13	36.1	108	63.9
Amphibia	—	—	8	11.9	7	14.3	1	2.8	16	9.5
Bufo americanus	—	—	8	11.9	7	14.3	1	2.8	16	9.5
Aves (including eggs)	2	11.8	16	23.9	6	12.2	4	11.1	28	16.6
Galliformes	1	5.9	5	7.5	4	8.2	2	5.6	12	7.1
Phasianus colchicus (egg)	—	—	2	3.0	—	—	—	—	2	1.2
Gallus gallus	1	5.9	3	4.5	4	8.2	2	5.6	10	5.9
Columbiformes	—	—	—	—	1	2.0	—	—	1	0.6
Zenaidura macroura	—	—	—	—	1	2.0	—	—	1	0.6
Strigiformes	—	—	1	1.5	—	—	—	—	1	0.6
Strigidae (feathers)	—	—	1	1.5	—	—	—	—	1	0.6
Passeriformes	1	5.9	12	17.9	2	4.1	2	5.6	15	8.9
Cyanocitta cristata	1	5.9	—	—	—	—	—	—	1	0.6
Corvus brachyrhynchos	—	—	1	1.5	—	—	—	—	1	0.6
Sturnella magna	—	—	1	1.5	—	—	—	—	1	0.6
Pipilo erythrophthalmus	—	—	1	1.5	—	—	—	—	1	0.6
Agelaius phoeniceus	—	—	1	1.5	—	—	—	—	1	0.6
Unidentified Feathers	—	—	7	10.4	2	4.1	2	5.6	11	6.5
Unidentified Eggs	—	—	1	1.5	—	—	—	—	1	0.6
Nonpasserine Forms	—	—	2	3.0	1	2.0	—	—	3	1.8
Unidentified Feathers	—	—	1	1.5	1	2.0	—	—	2	1.2
Unidentified Eggs	—	—	1	1.5	—	—	—	—	1	0.6
Mammalia	10	58.8	44	65.7	26	53.1	9	25.0	89	52.7
Insectivora	1	5.9	2	3.0	—	—	1	2.8	4	2.4

Table C (Continued)

FOOD ITEM	WINTER (17) No.	%	SPRING (67) No.	%	SUMMER (49) No.	%	AUTUMN (36) No.	%	TOTALS (169) No.	%
Blarina brevicauda	–	–	2	3.0	–	–	1	2.8	3	1.8
Scalopus aquaticus	1	5.9	–	–	–	–	–	–	1	0.6
Lagomorpha	4	23.5	4	6.0	5	10.2	2	5.6	15	8.9
Sylvilagus floridanus	4	23.5	4	6.0	5	10.2	2	5.6	15	8.9
Rodentia	7	41.2	44	65.7	23	46.9	7	19.4	81	47.9
Citellus tridecemlineatus	–	–	3	4.5	2	4.1	1	2.8	6	3.6
Peromyscus maniculatus	1	5.9	1	1.5	–	–	2	5.6	4	2.4
Peromyscus leucopus	–	–	–	–	1	2.0	–	–	1	0.6
Peromyscus sp.	4	23.5	18	26.9	8	16.3	–	–	30	17.8
Microtus pennsylvanicus	–	–	7	10.4	3	6.1	4	11.1	14	8.3
Microtus sp.	1	5.9	8	11.9	10	20.4	1	2.8	20	11.8
Mus musculus	1	5.9	2	3.0	–	–	–	–	3	1.8
Carnivora	15	88.2	65	97.0	43	87.8	34	94.4	157	92.9
Mephitis mephitis	15	88.2	65	97.0	43	87.8	34	94.4	157	92.9
Felis domesticus	2	11.8	1	1.5	–	–	–	–	3	1.8
Artiodactyla	–	–	3	4.5	2	4.1	1	2.8	6	3.6
Sus scrofa	–	–	3	4.5	2	4.1	1	2.8	6	3.6
PLANTS	14	82.4	64	95.5	44	89.8	34	94.4	156	92.3
Pinaceae	–	–	2	3.0	–	–	–	–	2	1.2
Picea abies	–	–	2	3.0	–	–	–	–	2	1.2
Gramineae	10	58.8	58	86.6	41	83.8	33	91.8	142	84.1
Bromus sp.	–	–	4	6.0	2	4.1	5	13.9	11	6.5
Festuca sp.	–	–	4	6.0	–	–	1	2.8	5	3.0
Poa pratensis & P. compressa	5	29.4	46	68.7	32	65.3	29	80.6	112	66.3
Hordeum sp.	–	–	1	1.5	–	–	1	2.8	2	1.2

	Col 1 No.	Col 1 %	Col 2 No.	Col 2 %	Col 3 No.	Col 3 %	Col 4 No.	Col 4 %	Col 5 No.	Col 5 %
Avena sativa	—	—	5	7.5	6	12.2	4	11.1	15	8.9
Sporobolus sp.	—	—	1	1.5	—	—	—	—	1	0.6
Agrostis sp.	—	—	1	1.5	—	—	—	—	1	0.6
Digitaria sp.	1	5.9	—	—	1	2.0	—	—	1	0.6
Paspalum ciliatifolium	—	—	—	—	—	—	—	—	1	0.6
Panicum sp.	2	11.8	17	25.4	10	20.4	20	55.6	47	27.8
Echinochloa crusgalli	5	29.4	3	4.5	3	6.1	2	5.6	10	5.9
Setaria sp.	1	5.9	12	17.9	7	14.3	9	25.0	33	19.5
Cenchrus sp.	—	—	—	—	—	—	—	—	1	0.6
Zea mays (stalks)	—	—	2	3.0	2	4.1	4	11.1	8	4.7
Zea mays (kernels)	—	—	1	1.5	1	2.0	—	—	2	1.2
Juglandaceae	1	5.9	—	—	—	—	—	—	1	0.6
Carya sp.	1	5.9	—	—	—	—	—	—	1	0.6
Fagaceae	1	5.9	—	—	—	—	—	—	1	0.6
Quercus sp.	1	5.9	—	—	—	—	—	—	1	0.6
Ulmaceae	—	—	—	—	2	4.1	—	—	2	1.2
Ulmus americana	2	11.8	—	—	2	4.1	—	—	2	1.2
Polygonaceae	2	11.8	10	14.9	10	20.4	9	25.0	31	18.3
Rumex sp.	—	—	—	—	1	2.0	—	—	1	0.6
Polygonum aviculare	—	—	—	—	1	2.0	—	—	1	0.6
Polygonum pensylvanicum	2	11.8	10	14.9	8	16.3	9	25.0	29	17.2
Polygonum persicaria	—	—	3	4.5	—	—	—	—	3	1.8
Polygonum convolvulus	—	—	1	1.5	—	—	—	—	1	0.6
Polygonum scandens	—	—	4	6.0	—	—	—	—	4	2.4
Chenopodiaceae	2	11.8	7	10.4	—	—	1	2.8	10	5.9
Chenopodium album	2	11.8	7	10.4	—	—	1	2.8	10	5.9
Amaranthaceae	—	—	5	7.5	3	6.1	—	—	8	4.7
Amaranthus spinosus	—	—	5	7.5	3	6.1	—	—	8	4.7
Caryophyllaceae	—	—	1	1.5	—	—	—	—	1	0.6

Table C (Continued)

Food Item	Winter (17)		Spring (67)		Summer (49)		Autumn (36)		Totals (169)	
	No.	%	No.	%	No.	%	No.	%	No.	%
Cerastium sp.	—	—	1	1.5	—	—	—	—	1	0.6
Cruciferae	—	—	2	3.0	—	—	—	—	2	1.2
Brassica sp.	—	—	1	1.5	—	—	—	—	1	0.6
Sisymbrium officinale	—	—	1	1.5	—	—	—	—	1	0.6
Rosaceae	1	5.9	6	9.0	5	10.2	1	2.8	13	7.7
Potentilla norvegica	—	—	1	1.5	—	—	—	—	1	0.6
Rubus sp.	—	—	—	—	1	2.0	—	—	1	0.6
Rosa sp.	—	—	5	7.5	2	4.1	—	—	7	4.1
Prunus serotina (bark)	—	—	—	—	—	—	1	2.8	1	0.6
Prunus serotina (seeds)	—	—	—	—	2	4.1	—	—	2	1.2
Prunus sp. (plums)	1	5.9	—	—	1	2.0	—	—	2	1.2
Leguminosae	2	11.8	7	10.4	13	26.6	10	27.8	32	18.9
Trifolium sp.	2	11.8	2	3.0	5	10.2	—	—	9	5.3
Medicago sativa	—	—	6	9.0	9	18.4	10	27.8	25	14.8
Unidentified Seed	1	5.9	—	—	—	—	—	—	1	0.6
Geraniaceae	—	—	1	1.5	—	—	—	—	1	0.6
Geranium carolinanum	—	—	1	1.5	—	—	—	—	1	0.6
Aceraceae	1	5.9	—	—	—	—	—	—	1	0.6
Acer negundo	1	5.9	—	—	—	—	—	—	1	0.6
Malvaceae	—	—	—	—	1	2.0	—	—	1	0.6
Malva neglecta	—	—	—	—	1	2.0	—	—	1	0.6
Solanaceae	4	23.6	14	20.9	3	6.1	5	13.9	26	15.4
Solanum nigrum	1	5.9	7	10.4	1	2.0	5	13.9	14	8.3
Solanum carolinense	3	17.6	3	4.5	1	2.0	—	—	7	4.1
Physalis heterophylla	—	—	4	6.0	1	2.0	—	—	5	3.0

	No.	%	No.	%	No.	%	No.	%	No.	%
Datura stramonium	—	—	2	3.0	—	—	—	—	2	1.2
Plantaginaceae	—	—	1	1.5	—	—	—	—	1	0.6
Plantago major	—	—	1	1.5	—	—	—	—	1	0.6
Compositae	1	5.9	3	4.5	9	18.4	5	13.9	18	10.7
Solidago sp.	—	—	1	1.5	—	—	—	—	1	0.6
Erigeron divaricatus	—	—	1	1.5	2	4.1	—	—	3	1.8
Ambrosia bidentata	—	—	—	—	1	2.0	—	—	1	0.6
Ambrosia trifida	—	—	1	1.5	—	—	—	—	1	0.6
Ambrosia artemisiifolia	1	5.9	—	—	3	6.1	1	2.8	5	3.0
Bidens sp.	—	—	1	1.5	3	6.1	4	11.1	8	4.7
Arctium minus	—	—	1	1.5	—	—	—	—	1	0.6
Cirsium sp.	—	—	—	—	1	2.0	2	5.6	3	1.8
UNIDENTIFIED SEEDS	3	17.6	6	9.0	7	14.3	3	8.3	19	11.2
FUNGI	—	—	1	1.5	1	2.0	—	—	2	1.2
PLANT FIBERS & WOOD CHIPS	17	100.0	58	86.6	41	83.7	33	91.7	149	88.2
INERT AND MISCELLANEOUS										
THREAD (COTTON)	—	—	2	3.0	—	—	—	—	2	1.2
GLASS	—	—	1	1.5	—	—	—	—	1	0.6
SAND	12	70.6	51	76.1	24	48.9	9	25.0	96	56.8
TRAP BAIT (DOG FOOD)	6	35.3	2	3.0	1	2.0	—	—	9	5.3

INDEX